Your Life Is Worth It!

Your Life Is Worth It!

Dedicated to the Underdog and the Overcomer

An Anthology

Dr. Marsie Ross – Visionary

Published by EdLyn Press

Washington, DC

Table of Contents

Your Life Is Worth It!

Introduction from the Visionary
Dr. Marsie Ross
Certified Integrative Nutrition Health Coach

I imagine you reading this book many years from now when my life cycle is long over. I'm convinced that even after the amazing women in this book have lived a full and whole life, what they've shared within these pages will live on.

I imagine you learning about the pandemic that took the lives of thousands of people worldwide in history books. You'll learn all about the virus that infected hundreds of thousands of people, shut down the world and shook the economy. At the time I'm writing this, we've been living with this new reality of social isolation, mandates, and fear for more than two years. But the truth is, the pandemic was the catalyst to the unveiling of what many of us were infected with long before COVID-19 struck the nation.

The government shut down and mandated home quarantine forced us to face the stark and very harsh reality of the "state of the world." Sitting at home, this reality quite literally hit "home" like a ton of bricks. For women, this rang true in a very deep and profound way.

If you're reading this in present day, you understand what I mean.

✓ The reality that we have been struggling to find our way in some capacity of our lives.
✓ The reality that we have mastered masking our pain in our "fake it till you make it" society.

✓ The reality that we have fully embraced the "secure the bag" approach to getting ahead.

Along the way, many of us discovered we lost our sense of self, our grounding center. So, you can guess what happened during those hours, days, months, and now years of solitude or, at the very least, a life without all the distractions. Yup! As my big mama used to say, our "chickens came home to roost!"

But in this season of release and reconciliation, something beautiful also happened to so many of us:

✓ We remembered we were created to thrive and survive together.
✓ We remembered we were created to be extraordinary.
✓ We remembered we were worthy of love, abundance, and peace.

But most importantly, we remembered we have the divine power to ***"be,"*** which does not have to translate into constantly ***"doing."***

We rediscovered that this human journey paves the way for us to grow and expand. It is in the being that gives us compassion and empathy for our fellow humans. It is in the being that we evolve into our highest selves.

This is when **_you_** discover that **_you_** are very necessary, and **_you_** are here to be AND do amazing things. This is when the underdog becomes the overcomer.

This is why I'm convinced this book will transcend time.

Because it will always serve as a reminder to you that YOUR LIFE IS WORTH IT!

About the Visionary

Dr. Marsie Ross is a women's wellness expert, best-selling author, Certified Integrative Nutrition Health Coach, international speaker, and executive producer and host of the *Live Well Beyond The Scale* podcast.

Dr. Marsie empowers women 40+ to successfully ditch diet dependency so they can create a wellness lifestyle on their own terms. Dr. Marsie has been featured on multiple national platforms, including NBC, ABC, and The Huffington Post. She is the founder of **The Well Woman Academy**™, a cultivated community designed for women over 40.

Hello@DrMarsie.com
Social Handle: @DrMarsie

Your Bloom is Worth It
Dr. Tiffany H. Taft
Certified Natural Health & Womb Wellness Coach

"Every soul is to be cherished; every flower is to bloom."
~Alice Walker

To everything, a season, a reason, a lifetime. How many times have we heard those phrases? But if we sit back and think about it, there is some level of truth in the sentiments. The problem is, we don't want to believe it to be true. But we all know that we are worth it and that we are each born with unique traits and gifts that only we were destined to share and serve. I don't know about you, but when I look back over my life so far, there are several lessons that I have had to learn that were not always easy but certainly worth it if I am being honest. Now, that is not to say that some experiences were just hard and I would even say, unfair. But the truth is ***every*** lesson is part of a story I was chosen to live to tell. So, no matter what hand you have been dealt, please know that you were only one built to live and tell it.

The unfortunate truth is life is not always fair, enjoyable, and sometimes it can even feel purposeless. The truth is, things come up, and life takes us through challenges; however, we must continue to rise above our circumstances. We must move into a place where we fully believe our lives are worth it. By now, you may be looking at these pages thinking, "girl, life is hard, and I am always getting the short end of the stick." Trust me. I hear you. I, too, have been there more often than I care to even focus time or attention on. But I want to bring your attention to a very powerful word that has been a game-changer for me. And that word is "choices." With this word in mind, let's ***choose*** to look at things differently. Why? Because life is about choices and the decisions we make, whether they be good, bad, or indifferent. It's a consciousness thing. Some of us choose to show up and participate *in* life, while others allow others and life to happen *to* them. There's a funny thing that happens when you **CHOOSE** to show up for yourself and empower yourself to move differently.

Are you ready to live empowered by your choices?

First, you must ***believe*** that ***you*** are worth it. I mean, really believe it. You must feel it in every part of your being. I remember when this was a hard pill for me to swallow because I felt everything that could go wrong was going wrong for me and that I somehow deserved it. Where did that thinking come from anyway? Was it something I was told as a child, or did it come from within? Why did I believe I didn't deserve more or better? After doing the work I'm sharing with you now, here's what I know for sure, we were not born to quit. We were born to thrive. Repeat after me…" I AM wired for excellence." As for me, I had to believe and encourage myself. I had to know that this place of despair would not be mine forever. I have long lived with the spiritual sickness of FEAR. This has been heavy, and only recently have I truly begun the journey to releasing that spiritual sickness. It has been a death grip on my being. But I have always known that at the core it is NOT who I am. I absolutely believe we were not designed in the spirit of fear. So how did I get there? It took time and still takes time. This is not a one-and-done project. So, over time as you grow, you may have to refine your practices to remind yourself just why you are worth it.

If you are feeling stuck in a rut and looking for your bloom, here are seven quick reasons right now to believe that **YOU ARE WORTH IT**. I've followed these steps myself to change my life and my mindset about my purpose and my power. I've helped other women, and now I want to help you find your bloom. All you must do is choose to believe and move towards the life you desire. I promise to be right there with you to guide and cheer you on if you do.

For context, blooming here is defined as a healthy, energetic, attractive countenance from the inside out.

Let's bloom together…

1. *You give your all* – You're the doer of "all the things" for all the people in your life but be honest, you're exhausting yourself. Are you really giving any of that time for you to "do you"? If you're not, is it because you don't even feel that you are worth it? From this point forward, let me permit you to prioritize yourself. *YOUR LIFE IS WORTH IT!*

2. *You are different* – This is okay because remember I said that every person is unique and born with their own set of gifts and talents that only they can contribute to the world. There is NO ONE else in the world like you. Isn't that a beautiful thing? Be honest. How can you shine if you are doing what everyone else is doing? You stand out, and that is EVERYTHING. *YOUR LIFE IS WORTH IT!*

3. *You help others* – You never know who's watching you. You live authentically, lead courageously, and inspire and empower others to do the same. Continue to give from a place of wholeness because when you are whole, you are helping others to bloom from your overflow. You are sought out for your gifts, talents, expertise, and your shine. You may never know who is inspired by YOU. *YOUR LIFE IS WORTH IT!*

4. *You are an advocate for growth* – You love to see others grow. Inspire them to embrace their unique gifts as you support and advocate for their expansion. You support them in finding their voice and standing in their truths confidently. There are no shadows, just complete lightness in their evolution. YOU are a rare find. *YOUR LIFE IS WORTH IT!*

5. *You make a difference* – Love yourself and be the change. *YOUR LIFE IS WORTH IT!*

6. *You care* – You're more than enough, and you encourage others through your caring that they too are different, and it is okay because they are worth it too. *YOUR LIFE IS WORTH IT!*

7. *You are for the community and before competition* – You value and put community first, and there is no spirit of competition. *YOUR LIFE IS WORTH IT!*

So, what have we learned from these quick reminders of why YOUR LIFE IS WORTH IT? It all starts with YOU! Pour into you so that you may give to others from the overflow. Yes, life gets hard and will challenge your patience but trust the process that allows you to prevail. Once you believe it, trust it, know it, then you will THRIVE in every aspect of your life. I by no means have had it easy through life and but even through my times of trouble, I know this for sure, I AM WORTH IT. So, what do I mean by that? I mean, I know that I AM enough. I know that I feel good about myself, and I'm happy. No, every day is not perfect, but when you know your life is worth it, you become less and less obsessed with perfection. I AM perfectly imperfect. There is a time to LIVE, BE, LEARN, and REFLECT. So many of us have lived a life of hurt, pain, and traumas of unspeakable kinds. But because we're born to thrive, we often seek peace in spaces that allow us to not only sit still but also to reflect on what matters most. In these moments, we can embrace the reality of our blessings. And when we resurface, renew, and refill, we can give to someone still experiencing their challenges and perhaps their darkest hour. When we have an overflow, we can lift them. Why? Because when you help others and focus on their needs, you experience the gift of compassion and a blessing that unlocks doors and opportunities you didn't even see coming. Dare to be the light.

Our lives can be put into buckets of time that just often get away from us. When we think of what makes us most happy and what we need, we begin to realize all the reasons why we are so worthy, and our life IS worth it. I know it is hard not to compare ourselves to others and wonder why it may appear that we're living a life of lies at times. Like, for real, what you see of people's public lives, may not be their *actual* life at all. If we want to live in our truth, we must stop comparing and realize that we all have our "stuff" and that life is not always as it appears. The best way forward is to focus on you and believe that you are uniquely and wonderfully made.

So, what makes a life worth it, you ask? A life that is FULL of giving and service to others. It is a life of giving but not at the expense of ourselves. This life is meant to be shared in connection and not isolation. When I look back now, I can reflect on parts of my life when I wanted to give up and questioned "why all of this bad stuff happening to me?" When I cried, no one responded to me. When I was in need, no one helped. I have played the blame game, felt empty and alone, and wondered why I didn't have certain things. I thought there must be more to this life. Did you know that we must be careful of the words we say to ourselves and the thoughts that we have? These things play a huge part in shifting our reality. While it is true that life is happening and bad things happen to good people, the goal is not to get stuck in sadness and repeat the cycle.

So, the reason I wrote this chapter and named it "**<u>Your Life is in BLOOM</u>**" is to remind us all, that like flowers and trees and nature in general, we humans too have a season, a reason, a lifetime to figure it out and get it right. We all have a job, a calling in our lives and for our lives. There is a time and place for everything, and nature knows the exact time to shine. Humans are a bit more complicated in this cycle of life, but please know there is a season that we will shine and a season that we will be crushed and prepared for our BLOOM. When we think of something or someone blooming, we think about something that peaks at an ideal moment. It is in a state of producing, thriving, or strength. They are growing and becoming their true beautiful selves and sharing their souls for the world to see. It is the essence of being. We are all BLOOM*ING*.

So often, we feel we're missing out on life because we may be working, raising a family, building a business, going to school, and driving kids around from place to place. When do we get to be and do for ourselves? Be honest right now. When was the last time that you did something JUST FOR YOU? No one else. Just you? If you can't remember, this is a great time to change that narrative and create a new story that shouts, I AM WORTH IT, and I deserve to have, do, or be…fill in the blank. Remember, I am not necessarily talking about the material things, although it's nice, and we all enjoy them. I'm talking about the things that add actual value to your lives and the lives you touch around you. These are the things that are priceless and irreplaceable. What is that for you?

Here's what it is for me. First, my *TIME* (being fully present for what matters most, not wasteful, is invaluable). Second, my *PEACE* (a place of wholeness and completeness), and then my *COMMUNITY* (how I choose to show up in service, be remembered, and share what was given to me as a gift). Sometimes, when we focus on only the material things, that still leaves us empty and chasing the next big thing to make us feel worthy. But does it? Or does it trap us into a false sense of security? Remember,

BLOOM*ING* has nothing to do with riches or physical trappings but everything to do with morals, right relationships, alignment, and timing. Be patient, my dear. It's coming. When you've done the work, the fruits of your labor will be more than you can handle. Take this time and continue to prepare to explode beyond your imagination. You don't have to be in the limelight or have all the outward recognition to know that you are impactful. Continue to show up for you and create those healthy boundaries.

So, what have we learned, and what are we willing to change to ensure that our cups are always full and overflowing with unlimited opportunities, possibilities, and intentions that we have attracted on purpose?

Let me remind you (us):

1. You are unique, and no one can outshine you. So LIVE life fully and from the overflow! Bloom where you are planted and sow where you are fed.
2. You MUST put yourself first, and this is not being selfish, but rather, it is necessary. Therefore, do something that feeds your Soul.
3. You are worthy of the best. "Let blessings fall like blossoms all around you" (Rumi). Be in pursuit of that thing that proves that you are worthy every day.

Finally, life offers us great opportunities for PAUSE. In those moments, we find our peace and our purpose and the reasons why deeply OUR LIVES ARE WORTH IT!

And just like I promised, I'm right there with you. So, reach out to me or check out my website, join my community, and get more tools and guidance directly from me.

Be Still. Be Healed. Be Well.

ABOUT THE AUTHOR

Dr. Tiffany Taft is the Chief Wellness Officer and owner of Sacred Soul Wellness where she is focused on womb wellness and creating remarkable holistic experiences that empower women to be the best WHOLE version of themselves. She educates women on how to heal, inspire, and equip themselves with life-long tools that supports them at every phase of womanhood. She is an Integral Healer utilizing ancient wisdom to counter dis-ease in the body, mind, and soul. She supports women through the phases of the sacred moon of fertility, pregnancy, and beyond. Her approach is the perfect mix of ancient wisdom and modern science. Dr. Tiffany creates Sacred Spaces of healing for her clients and promotes a healthy balance of body, breath, and movement that restores relief from chronic pain and issues that have left years of pain and traumas unhealed. Dr. Tiffany offers in person and virtual services for those looking to deepen their journey to wholeness. She encourages us all to BE STILL. BE HEALED. BE WELL!

www.sacredsoulwellness.org

Social Handle: @sacredsoulwellness

Your Vision is Worth It
April Chenier
Therapeutic Vision Board Facilitator

In 2014, my best friend suggested we throw a vision board party. At the time, we never imagined where this journey would take us. Vision board parties were all the rage, and as a collage artist for 25 years, I was a bit smug about the whole thing. I didn't know much about vision boards, but from what I'd assumed based on no actual experience, I thought they were big, ugly, and trivial. All I thought was you get a white poster board and put **a bunch** of things on it - a new car, a new house, money, vacations, and a new husband. Then what? *Voila*? All these things would magically happen because I cut out some pictures and glued them to a poster board? I didn't buy it, and it seemed like a waste of time. So, I put my bestie off. She is, however, very persuasive, and we eventually had the party.

We planned it for the first weekend in January 2015 to encourage our friends to join us while they might be putting their new year's resolutions into practice.

We went about sending invitations and gathering supplies. As our friends began to RSVP, I decided that I'd better start creating a vision board of my own. I LATER REALIZED what I did next would become the blueprint for running my "Expand Your Vision" workshops today. Here's what I did.

I took a few days to think about my vision board. I decided that if I was going to take the time to do it, I might as well make it meaningful. So, I started asking myself questions—What did I want to work on in my life? What is important to me now? And as I thought more about these questions, my intentions started to take shape. That's when I decided to map my board and break things down into sections. I took a large foam core board and cut it vertically in half. I wanted my intentions displayed with the most important at the top, each flowing into the next, working their way down to the bottom.

In 2014 these were my intentions:
1. Overcome my fear of flying
2. Rekindle my love life
3. Secure a new home
4. Continue to nurture my relationship with my Higher Power
5. Social life

The Power of the Vision Board

Fear of Flying

Let me start by saying I haven't always been afraid of flying. As a kid and into adulthood, I flew all the time. My parents are from California and moved to Maryland when I was two, so we were always flying to California and back to visit relatives during holidays and summer break. So, for many years, flying was a normal part of my life. In 2005, while on an impromptu trip to New York, I reunited with my old college friend, and that visit would be the start of a whirlwind romance that led to marriage and two amazing kids. While we dated, we planned several romantic getaways from Bermuda to San Francisco, so flying was an exciting part of our life together.

In 2008 something changed. We welcomed our first child into the world. Becoming a mother brought many new emotions, including a paralyzing, irrational fear of flying. This gripping fear completely halted any trips that required me to get on an airplane. Instead, I believed it would be safer to travel to locations we could drive rather than risk plunging to our deaths in a plane. Looking back, it sounds dramatic, but that fear for me was real!

Love Life

In 2014, I was married with two small children, a girl, and a boy, aged six and three, and intimacy with my husband gradually dwindled. I was beginning to feel disconnected, and I felt very strongly that rekindling that spark of desire between us would point us in the direction of becoming closer as a couple. Because this was my second marriage, I understood the reality that lack of intimacy, both physical and emotional, could end relationships. So, I was determined to prioritize this intention and include it as a focus on my vision board.

New Home

When my best friend and I were planning our vision board party, my family and I lived in my father's house. My dad moved to an apartment in Washington, DC, to be closer to work and experience city life. He offered to have us stay in the family home while he went off to explore. My daughter is autistic, and we lived in Baltimore City at the time. We were very concerned with the level of education she would receive as a student with special needs. When the opportunity to move to a bigger space in a better school district, we couldn't refuse. My family had been at my dad's house for a year when our marriage started going south. My husband was feeling intense pressure living in a house that was not his own, which took a toll on our relationship. I knew finding a new home for us in a good neighborhood in the same zone as my daughter's school was imperative. So, I added finding a new home as the third section of my vision board.

Relationship with God

I love my relationship with God, and silly as it seems now, during those times of stress, I had turned away from Him. I had stopped getting up early to start my day with meditation and prayer. So, it was important to me to include spirituality on my vision board to have a constant reminder.

Social Life

When I go back and look at that very first vision board, I made all those years ago, down at the bottom, I see now that I planted some seeds, I had no idea how they would grow. At that time, I had a wonderful social life. I belonged to a book club that has been in existence for over 20 years, and I have a wonderful group of close friends who I saw and still see regularly. There was no need for a social section on my vision board. When I reflect on it now, I wanted to make sure that I stayed in touch with my friends that I was intentional about keeping a social calendar even with all the issues at home and raising two small children.

How it all came together

Now that I've laid out the intentions on my vision board, let me explain how they manifested for me quickly and how others continue to come to life years after I put it together.

By the end of 2014, life started to shift and move for me. And that's when I learned a powerful lesson: vision boards are ***not*** a frivolous waste of time. Instead, they are powerful tools that help you grow and change in ways you never imagined when done with intention.

My best friend and I gave our vision board party, and it was a huge success. All our friends were there, the food was amazing, and the drinks were plentiful. We had a full house! We decorated the tables with white tablecloths; each person had a stack of fresh magazines, a board, and a pair of scissors at their station. I scattered some of my pre-cut images and words in the middle of each table for our guests to use. We both welcomed everyone to our event. I nervously spoke about my vision board, sharing my method and technique with everyone. The party lasted several hours. I noticed that instead of the lively, loud chatter of a room full of women fresh into the new year, the room was quiet, save for the music we had playing in the background. Everyone was focused. They were taking this seriously. This activity was not a joke to our guests. I didn't know what to make of it, and for a few years after the party, I was always surprised at the quiet in the room when I facilitated what was to become my signature **Expand Your Vision** workshop. As we wrapped up for the night, put the food away, and folded up the rented tables and chairs, I decided to take my vision board up to my bedroom so that I could see it every day. I wanted to test out the theory of manifesting your intentions through vision boards, and I knew that it couldn't if my work sat in the basement.

I placed my board on my nightstand, unframed, leaning against the wall. I could see it every time I entered or exited my bedroom. I could see it every time I came out of my bathroom. I could see it every time I reached for something on the nightstand.

Sometimes I would stand in front of it for minutes at a time, thinking about how good it looked, focusing on the images I had so carefully placed, daydreaming about a life that had shifted into a better place. Other times it was just in my periphery. Days, sometimes weeks, would go by without me intentionally focusing on it. My busy life consumed me at times, and I could not take even a few moments to gaze at this work of art that I had made. What I did not know at that time was that my vision board was "working." The simple fact that it was visible in my bedroom and that even those short glances at it counted in serious ways.

I noticed later that I was tired of cars and road trips. I wanted to go somewhere...on a plane. The top of my vision board representing my fear of flying is full of blue skies, fluffy white clouds, a glittery golden sun, and words of in-flight encouragement. "No Crazy Worries," "Perfect flight," "I want to get out of town." and "Where is the best place you've ever gone on vacation?" take up prime space on this board that helped me to push myself forward and book two tickets to Puerto Rico for my husband and me. Although I did have to book a non-stop flight, take two night-time ibuprofens, and drink a bloody Mary before we got on the plane, I did it! I felt like I was on my way to overcoming my irrational fear. We flew several more times that year and, in the years, since. I confess, I'm still skittish about flying, but I'm not refusing to travel if I must get on a plane. I have my rituals, prayer, deep breaths, and I never listen to news stories about plane crashes. This year I traveled to Miami, and I was totally fine!

Just beneath the section on my fear of flying is Rekindle My Love life. I booked our trip to Puerto Rico to start the process of overcoming my fear of flying and injecting more passion into my marriage. I included images and words on my board that made me feel sexy and desirable. Even though I rarely wear it, I love leopard print. It feels wild and uninhibited to me. I covered the background of this section in leopard print and layered over top of it symbols that represented a super-hot relationship I had in my younger single days. I was feeling out of touch with that part of myself. Remembering who I was in that prior experience reminded me of who I wanted to be with my husband when we could steal time away for just the two of us. We had a great time on our trip! There were a few hiccups, but we worked those out and enjoyed ourselves. Unfortunately, when we returned, we quickly devolved into our old routine. There was, however, a silver lining to this, but it came much later. This may seem like a strange thing to share but, I've always considered myself sexy and desirable. And for me, it felt frustrating and unnatural to have sex and intimacy with my husband as part of a vision board. But, when I glued down those images and words that represented another time in my life, something manifested that was unexpected. I unlocked a door inside myself that opened.

It was a very slow process with this old relationship. At first, my old flame and I would reach out to wish each other a happy birthday or to check-in. Initially, our communications were maybe twice a year, but they became more frequent over time, once every few months. And I enjoyed those chats very much! We developed a refreshingly platonic relationship despite our clear attraction to each other through these conversations.

My marriage eventually came to an end. We separated in 2020, and the air between us is better than it's been in years. Without the pressure of sexual intimacy and daily interaction, we are experiencing newfound freedom as co-parents in this next phase of our relationship. The images I used to represent a passionate love life to recapture a spirit of sexy inhibition with my husband manifested itself as a deeper relationship with a man I mainly had a physical attraction. We're friends today, and I love this new aspect of our friendship. I could never have imagined things going this way. Although, I attribute this to my vision board working quietly in the background of my life.

The last section on my vision board is my social life. All the images and words are related to friendship, being a better friend, entertaining friends, listening, and not talking so much, meeting and entertaining new friends. Those closest to me know that I don't have much interest in meeting new people to make friends. Although I have incredibly close relationships, starting new ones doesn't come easily. Revisiting my intentions from 2014 while writing this chapter has given me another a-ha! moment with my work as a therapeutic vision board facilitator. I can see that the social section were seeds that I planted, and they have bloomed into Expand Your Vision! I call my workshop Expand Your Vision because I have witnessed vision boards open the mind and spirit to make adjustments and shifts in your life in ways that are more than the literal image you select to put on your vision board. In 2014, I just wanted to have functions for my friends and make new friends. I had no idea that a thriving business would grow out of my desire at that moment to entertain. I honestly never thought that what I put on my vision board would be so powerful or continue to work long after I had relegated it to a space on the wall in my studio as a piece of art. Vision boards DO work! They can be used as a tool to make significant changes in your life. The key is visibility. If you can't see it, it can't work for you. But, if you take a few minutes every day to focus on your vision board, amazing things will happen, even those you never imagined.

ABOUT THE AUTHOR

April Chenier is a master collage artist and Therapeutic Vision Board Facilitator. She has developed the Expand Your Vision program using her personal technique which links the power of vision boards to an artful presentation that is unique to the practice. April curates Expand Your Vision workshops for coaches and therapists who want to add a powerful visual dynamic to enhance their program.

Aprilspaper@gmail.com

SOCIAL HANDLE: @expandyourvision_aprilspaper

Your Intimacy and Sexual Health is Worth It
Dr. Juan Michelle Martin
Pelvic Floor Physical Therapist and Sex Counselor

Let's talk about the seldom-discussed areas of life and health. While that can be many things, when we think about it, few things get swept under the rug, like the topic of sex. It's just not polite "table conversation." God forbid we talk about it outside of the context of life in our '20s and '30s. I mean, who do these kids think they are? Seriously! How do they think they got here? But I digress!

What happens in life is that as we get older, we somehow lose touch with ourselves. As women, we start families, become wives, run households, build careers, and when we hit the 40's and 50's, somehow the spunk and the spark are gone! There's a reason why the movie "How Stella got her groove back" and "Fifty Shades of Grey" made such an impact. There is typically a consensus that "sexiness" is tied to youth.

What happens as we age?
We need to consider not just the words "age," "sex," or "intimacy," but also the intersectionality of other aspects, like the mental, physical, and emotional coming into play. Somehow society has this predefined narrative that our 20s to early '30s are meant for child-rearing. Our 40's are where we're indebted to those we've reared, functioning more like a cleaning service and chauffeur, and after that, life somehow loses its zest. We get older, reach the "dreadful menopause," and then we wait our turn to slip into the abyss quietly. It's the most absurd thing, but somehow, that is how many women assume their lives will be. I'm here to tell you that we need to, and can, reimagine it all!

Let's start with the physical

I like to think of the journey more as maturation vs. aging. Sure, our 20's are supposedly when most people assume that we peak. From a hormonal perspective, sex hormones are high, fertility is usually great, and physically we seem to run on little to no sleep. But with time, pregnancy, and childbirth, we may experience physical changes, some wanted and some unwanted.

Then, hormones start to decline, and somewhere between our mid 40's and early 50's, we reach menopause. As it relates to intimacy, physical changes can impact how we view intimacy. For example, changes in the body, sensation, and appearance, to name a few. This can translate into changes in our level of appreciation for touch, intimacy, and sex itself.

From an emotional aspect, the assumption is that our emotional IQ improves with age, and we are somehow better able to handle all the things in this world as they come because of experience, know-how, and all of that. Am I right? Yet how we show up emotionally through the years also depends on many factors, including the physical, and when it comes to intimacy, there are many reasons why there may be some issues here.

Ultimately, our goal should never be to accept the narratives placed on us. We are the ones who define what our lives should be and understand that may be different for so many. Some women will enjoy a version of motherhood, whether they have conceived themselves, adopted, stayed at home, or continued advancing their careers while they parent. Some women will continue to climb career-wise and embark on entrepreneurship, doing big, bold things and seeking more adventure in their life. Some are content with a quieter style of life and solitude. Whatever your choices are, know that they are just that! Your choices. **The intersection of "who we are" and "our sexual selves."**

We mentioned earlier that as the numbers on our clock rise, we sometimes dissociate from who we are as intimate and sexual beings. Part of the reason for this is that we are complex individuals. We may be parents, wives/partners, employees, or employers. We may have other things that we love and have piqued our interests with time. We may be dealing with grief, loss, or other negative circumstances. The reality is that it is hard to separate the physical and non-physical in life. Realistically, when we think of intimate relationships, it's more than just physical. It's emotional; it's sensory. It's so much more than just the act of sex!

It doesn't help that they say that women are the more emotional beings. And guess what, that is ok because we don't do anything half-hearted; we put EVERYTHING we have and who we are into what we do. So, let's look at some different scenarios that happen in life that can change how we view intimacy and its impact on our lives.

Menopause

Menopause is the cessation of menses, otherwise known as periods. This usually occurs at around 51 and is characterized by the menses stopping for 12 consecutive months. This means if you stopped for seven months and then had another cycle, the countdown starts over yet again. When a woman goes through menopause, the sex hormones decrease, specifically estrogen. This can lend itself to many changes, including changes in the vaginal tissues, pain and/or sensory changes at the vulva, and pain with sex. For example, post-menopausal women are more prone to urinary tract infections because the decline in estrogen causes the pH in the vagina to increase. Now don't get me wrong, this does not happen to everyone, but it can impact quite a few people. In addition, these changes don't necessarily only happen with the immediate transition to menopause but can happen over the years after. Just think about it. Pain, tissue changes, maybe some other bowel or bladder changes, and now this goes from a physical issue to a complete damper on life itself.

Postpartum

Everyone knows that being pregnant is a huge transition in a woman's life. Ten months! That's how long it takes to grow and nurture that baby, and while doing so, the body goes through significant changes at the joints, muscles, connective tissues, and even with the hormones.

Then comes the birth, an experience that can vary with each delivery. And finally, the postpartum period, or life after birth. There is a saying, "Once postpartum, always postpartum!" It makes sense, right? You're always going to be a mom. When you enter the postpartum period, you need to consider the physical aspects and changes in the body. Let's not forget the emotional and psychological toll that being a new mom, or a newly postpartum mom brings. What about the support system? What about sleep? Yes, I said it! SLEEP! Lack of sleep will cause the body to not function at its best. When we look at all these components, the physical, emotional, psychological, and support system, it is easier to recognize that lack in any of these areas will affect a mom tremendously!

Physical Changes

Our last example is physical changes on account of age. Life changes can happen at any point, and our bodies can respond differently. There may be weight changes, whether increased or decreased. There may be hormonal changes. There may be sleep deprivation because of kids, work, and other responsibilities. Chronic disease also tends to be more prevalent as we age, hypertension, diabetes, arthritis, depression/ mental health issues, etc. Ultimately, you can gather from the examples above that, as women, our bodies can go through quite a lot. The problem is that it's not just physical. Think about all these things. Think about not controlling the bladder or the bowels as you wish. Think of having discomfort- I mean, who wants it!

And most importantly, think about the quality of life. Research has shown that painful intercourse (dyspareunia) is associated with a lower sexual quality of life, resulting in significant psychological and personal suffering (Arawak et al., 2020). This means that these incidents are not separate. Sexual changes can have a profound impact and can result in emotional distress and relationship distress, among other things.

How do we manage the changes that come with age and our sexual being?

So how do we begin to reconcile these issues? The changes that are happening and the negative impact on your sex life. We first must admit that there is an issue.

Unfortunately, sometimes the medical field has been dismissive regarding women's sexual issues in our society, resulting in many women going further down the rabbit-hole of emotional and psychological distress. There is a specific psychological impact when our bodies have failed to deliver on what they are meant to do. Just think. If you have always experienced pleasure with intimacy and now you can't, you're more likely to be affected by that. You will ask, "what the heck is happening to me!" Additionally, we are conditioned to think that sex should not be desirable as we age. We should not take an interest in our bodies as the negative things occurring are just par for the course. So, what are the beliefs we harbor regarding our bodies as we age, especially if the changes occurring are things we do not want to see? Does it cause us to shy away from others? From relationships? I remember having a client; let's call her "Mary" come to me after just having gone through menopause two years earlier. Mary said to me, "I try to hurry to bed at night and pull the covers up to pretend that I am sleeping to avoid any intimacy with my husband. I don't like my body, so how can he?" We had a lot of work to do! Like helping Mary understand that her worth was not tied to and should never be tied to the thoughts of others or even something like sex.

I'll say this over and over until I am blue in the face. As women, we bear a lot of responsibility. We play a lot of roles. However, one of those roles should always be taking care of ourselves. Being present for ourselves. Understanding that **WE ARE WORTH IT!** We are worth it at all times of our lives and regardless of what we are going through. And we owe it to ourselves to give ourselves enough grace to see ourselves through these times.

Sure, "life happens." As we get older, some things change, either for the good or the not-so-good, but we should always try to determine our goals. Even for sex! What is your goal for sex? Is it pleasure? Is it the big O? Are you just seeking intimacy? Or do you not even care about sex and would rather cuddle?

I always tell my clients: "You are responsible for your pleasure, and we need to ensure that we seek out ways to be empowered to do such. As a very action-oriented person, I'll take you through a few steps to help guide you in this direction. Remember, this is only the tip of the iceberg but a start to help ensure that you get on the path you desire.

Here are 5 Action Steps you can take to get your sex life back on track:

Step 1: Acknowledge that there is an issue
      I said it before. You know when something is wrong. Lean into that intuition. If it doesn't feel right, it's probably because it isn't right.

Step 2: Seek out professional help
      There are a few professionals who are well versed in all things sexual health. These are:

1. A sexual medical specialist or a medical doctor specializing in this can guide you in the right direction. Sometimes with the changes that we experience in our bodies, we may need a little help. In addition, there are times when specific medications may be warranted for everything to function as it should. A great resource is ISSWSH, International Society for the Study of Women's Sexual Health: https://www.isswsh.org/.
   By clicking the "find a provider" tab, you can search for vetted providers in your area.

2. A pelvic floor physical therapist. No one knows the muscles and the function of the pelvis better than a pelvic PT. In addition, we are versed in diagnosing and addressing the neurological and musculoskeletal components that could be disrupting your sex life.

3. A sex therapist. The sessions are more than talk therapy, honey! They dig deeper. They then give you the strategies to identify what things may be awry and what things you may need to change. These sessions can be done with or without your partner present and are extremely helpful in allowing individuals to identify what may be holding them back from intimacy and start taking steps towards correcting or addressing those things. Understand that you cannot and should not wait until your relationship fails to seek a sex therapist. When you recognize that there is a problem, reach out! AASECT, the American Association of Sexuality Educators, Counselors, and Therapists, is a great resource: https://www.aasect.org/referral-directory

These three specialists often work hand-in-hand with each other. Your joy is our concern, and the holistic approach is always best!

Step 3: Start journaling.

I always encourage individuals to journal. Sometimes, it doesn't register as it does on paper when it is in our minds. Write down your thoughts. Write down your goals. Write down your expectations. Then go after them!

Step 4: Open yourself up to explore.

This one gets a lot of people because they have never permitted themselves to be challenged in this area of discovery. This may look like exercises in touch, pleasure mapping, and other sensory-focused exercises to determine what feels good or doesn't feel good. There is a saying that goes, "you are responsible for your pleasure." I am not sure where I first heard it, but I agree. Identifying those things that you like, are comfortable with, and feel good is ideal and an excellent way for you to share with your partner to enjoy the sensory experience.

Similarly, opening to learn what your partner may like and explore new things together can be a fun and meaningful experience. This might be a bit much for some, and there may be other emotions at play. However, an exercise in self-appreciation like standing in a mirror, fully clothed to seeing yourself unclothed in a mirror and affirming your beauty, your magic, and the essence of who you are, might be a great start.

Step 5: Reconnect to self

Sometimes we all need to take a step back and recognize that WE ARE WORTH IT! Our life is worth it! With everything going on in our society on a large scale to our individual lives on a smaller but more personal scale, we sometimes need to take a step back and appreciate all we are. We must take time to reconnect to self and soul. Also, take time to acknowledge the beauty within and redefine your goals and trajectory. Regardless of what is happening, we need to take some time in reflection and gratitude and always continue to look forward to being whatever the best version of ourselves will be! Are you interested in more guidance and support from a licensed specialist?

ABOUT THE AUTHOR

Dr. Juan Michelle Martin Pelvic Floor Physical Therapist; Birth Doula; and Reproductive Wellness Coach who works with women from puberty through menopause to address issues related to the bowels, bladder, pelvic pain, pregnancy, and sexual function. It is her desire for women to live their best lives!

Dr. Martin is the owner of JMM Health Solutions, a private practice in the Atlanta metro area, the co-founder of the podcast, Fueling Her: A Woman's Guide to Wellness, a licensed and certified birth doula trainer with the National Black Doulas Association, a coach and mentor. In addition, she is the co-founder of The Black Female Foundation's business coaching program for minority women in business and The Pelvic PT Doulas, where she serves as an educator and business coach.

www.jmmhealthsolutions.com
Social Handle: @thepelvicperspective

Your Strength is Worth It
Tiffany Forte'
Certified Personal Trainer and Women's Fitness Coach

During a training session, I asked my client to look in the mirror and tell me something positive about herself. After a few seconds, she looked at me and quietly said, "I love that I'm very positive." I thought that maybe I wasn't as straightforward as I should've been because clearly, she didn't understand the assignment. So, I tried again. This time she looked at me and said, "I *think* I like my hair." Still not giving me what I asked. So, I tried again. This time I looked her in the eyes to ensure I had her full attention and told her to look at herself in the mirror and say something positive about herself. She said softly, "I like that I am a hard worker." Now, at this point, you may be thinking, "what does this crazy lady want?" And as you can imagine, both of us were getting a little frustrated too. But I was determined to find a way to break through to show off her "self-love" for me. So, I tried yet again. When she came up short another time, I wondered why it was so hard for her to look at herself and say something good. I was about to shout, "I'm asking you to say something about YOU," but then it finally hit me. She didn't have much to say because she didn't feel good about herself deep down. So, this time when I looked at her, I simply said, "I'm listening, sis."

Here's what I learned...

She was always the "fat friend" for most of her life. In her circle, she was the unattractive one, and like so many of us, she ate her feelings. After years of self-doubt and shame, her self-esteem was virtually nonexistent. After hearing this, I asked her if I could hug her, and with tears flowing, she said, "yes." Afterward, I asked her if I could help her with the assignment. Her "yes" came slightly slower this time, and her voice was lower. I took her hand, and we both looked in the mirror. I told her to look at herself. The person she is now. The woman is in the mirror now. She stared for several minutes. Then I said, tell _her_ one positive thing.

She finally said, "I love the way I look!"
We were both smiling from ear to ear.
I said… "LOUDER" And louder she was!
"I LOVE THE WAY I LOOK!"
"Even LOUDER," I said.
"I LOVE THE WAY I LOOK!"

That was such a breakthrough moment for her. As for me, I couldn't have been prouder to be her coach.

Sometimes we all need that person in our corner to remind us how far we've come and to push us past our comfort zone. Nothing extraordinary happens in the comfort zone. Not growth and not change. But one thing that I've learned in my years of training my clients is that to achieve physical strength you, must be mentally strong.

The girl she once was, was not the woman she is today physically. Her body has transformed, but mentally the overweight, sad, unmotivated girl was still standing in front of the mirror. It was hard for her to even believe she deserved to give herself such praise. In our sometimes-superficial world, we often judge people for what they look like on the outside, but let's be clear, you can look incredible on the outside and still be a mess on the inside. This is why my coaching program is so unique and has become highly sought after. I help my clients transform their mindset and let go of their false beliefs so they can transform their bodies _and_ their lives. Why? Because your mental strength is so important if you want to be your best you, Sis!

Let's dive in

It's time for the health industry to recognize mental health as physical health. You truly can't have one without the other. What you do physically starts with the motivation and the will to want to do better, but your mental strength makes you stick to your goals. When the road gets tough, your mental health is why you get through it. After all, you wanted that job, that degree, that family, that business, that 501c3 status, that car, and the path to get there wasn't always smooth, but you persevered. And your health is no different, and therefore it's also obtainable. Nothing is standing in your way except for you. The truth is, we are all capable of living a healthy lifestyle, the only difference is the journey to get there may look a little different from person to person. If you're ready to get your "mind right," follow the steps I've outlined below.

Know your why

When meeting clients for the first time, I always start with identifying their "why." Because we both must know you're about to go on a journey that will be filled with ups and downs. There's no doubt that you'll be met with struggles, and physical changes will feel like they're not coming fast enough. You may get frustrated. All those things are ok to feel and part of the process. But if you don't know why you may want to give up. And when I know your why, I won't let you give up! To put it plainly, I ask the *"why"* question to set the mental tone for my clients. My clients who ready their mental toughness early in the journey are the ones who are extremely successful in my program. So, my advice to you, before you start anything, **identify your why**.

Write it down

After you know your why, write down the specific goals you want to accomplish. Why, you ask? Because there is a science to seeing the things you want on paper. Studies show that writing things down can help you connect to your goals. In other words, it is a sure way to manifest them into reality. This is where your vision for your health takes form and when you write down your vision, it becomes clear and concise.

Put yourself on a timer and stick to it

Next, write down the start and end dates for those goals. This doesn't mean that you fail if you don't meet a deadline; far from it. You only fail at what you do not try. But there is nothing worse than sitting on a goal for years and achieving nothing. We've all been there or know a "friend" who has. Great ideas don't turn into reality unless there is a concrete timeline. Why, you ask? Because life happens. We get busy. Things come up, and poof! Our goals are now pushed to the back seat, and then three years later, we're still talking about that one goal that we never accomplished. Don't you want to stop letting that be the norm for your health?

Put it in plain sight

Finally, keep your goals posted somewhere visible. Why, you ask? Because it keeps you reminded of your why! Plus, it can be a constant reminder of why you can't quit. HINT: This helps during those tough days. Finally, there's no better way to stay on track than wake up in the morning and see your vision and goals every day.

Ok. Now that we talked about your goals let's talk about keeping you motivated to attack these goals.

I once heard that if you want to succeed, you must want it just as bad as you want to breathe. WOW! Talk about motivation!

Motivation

I hosted a health and fitness expo in June of 2021, and it was an incredible experience. Not just because I got to be creative and host this fitness event for women of color, but because of the obstacles I had to go through to make this event happen for my community. I was motivated by something bigger than me. Women got the chance to meet and support one another, that otherwise may never have gotten the chance if the event did not happen. It was beautiful to see. My motivation comes from these experiences. Knowing that I was cultivating something bigger than myself helped me be triumphant when it was not so easy to do so. Do you want to know how to find what motivates you?

What are you passionate about?

Tap into the things that keep you up at night! You know what I mean. What can't you stop thinking about? You may be wondering, "How does this tie into health?" To that, I say, "Great question!" Here's how. What we do in the gym directly relates to what we do outside of the gym. If you are motivated enough to start that non-profit for a cause near and dear to you, you can become just as motivated to find and stick to a health and wellness program that will improve your quality of life. It's about a greater purpose.

If you're looking for ideas to stay motivated, the first step is to take a hard look at your inner circle. Yes, sis, your inner circle is an excellent source for innovative ideas and inspiration. But be intentional and mindful. Everyone grows at a different pace, and you may risk people projecting their fears and insecurities onto you. This negativity can weigh you down and leave you discouraged, whether intended or unintended. Motivation is also connected to mental strength. Have you heard the saying, "The body does what the mind tells it to?" Staying on track comes down to monitoring your thoughts. With everything going on in the world and even in your home, it can be enough to derail and distract you. It's essential to keep an inventory of your feelings, and if something is throwing you off, it must go. Your peace and mental health are far too important to be disrupted. If you're still struggling with finding ways to stay motivated, I suggest taking a break.

"Tiff, are you suggesting I stop what I am doing? I thought I should be doing the opposite?"

Yup! You read that right. Not being motivated to do or accomplish whatever you need to can be due to having too much going on or just pure burnout. So yeah, take a break and draw inspiration on what moves you. For example, I got to a point where I was sick of my own business! I didn't want to train clients. I didn't want to book new ones. I for sure didn't want to read emails or update my website. I didn't want to do anything for my business. That's burnout. The best way to get over burnout is to avoid it at all costs. Another way to stay motivated is to make sure that your daily work is truly your passion. Sometimes when there is no cheer squad, no accolades, and no tangible incentives, the one thing to keep you moving is the pure accomplishment of working towards your goals and in your passion. However, this only works if your goal is one you truly want to accomplish. I have had several of those moments where just the thought of "Hey Tiff, get up so you can positively change someone's life today!" would get my hyped to deliver fitness solutions. We all know the benefits of consistent exercise and how black women are at such a high risk of cardiovascular-related illness. So yeah, just one workout is important, and at the very least, I show up for you, sis. My motivation truly comes from within, and it stems from living a life of unhealthy decisions, poor habits, being a slave to someone else's clock, and living an unfulfilled life. At the end of the day, sis, you must decide to live the life you want and on your terms. In the community of women I lead, we call that living happily.

Happy

When we talk about happiness, I've found it's such a relative word. Meaning it can mean so many different things according to who you ask. As you read this, I want you to reflect on your idea of happiness. Not mine. Not your momma's. Not your spouse's. What do _**you**_ want?

Before you answer, take a moment, and think.

What do "I" want…and, sis, no request is too big?

After all, there are people right now in this very moment living the life that you want to live. So now it's time to take action with the steps I gave you. Take a moment and jot down three things you want, three goals you want to accomplish, or a mix of the two. This is important because if you have no clue what you want, you will be on a lifetime journey searching for that missing piece; most importantly, you will never be truly happy. And how could you? You don't even know what happiness looks like, even if it slapped you across the face!

Goal 1:

Goal 2:

Goal 3:

Now that you have your three goals write down two to three steps to achieve them. Remember, you need actual steps to get to where you want to. Get specific here. Don't rush through this; we are talking about your happiness after all. Think GPS to your favorite destination spot (it's Jamaica for me)!

Steps to get to goal 1:

A.

B.

C.

Steps to get to goal 2:

A.

B.

C.

Steps to get to goal 3:

A.

B.

C.

Patience

Now that you have started your roadmap to living happily, keep in mind this won't happen overnight. I feel like that's an obvious thing to say, but because our culture has conditioned us to believe that things happen with a click of a button, I want to remind you that goals take time to create and manifest into reality. Sis, you must give it time. I want to address this because many people give up too darn early. Like, dang, it's only been a week, and just because you didn't hit six figures, you want to throw the entire business away. We must remove these unnecessary expectations and pressure from ourselves. You wonder why you aren't happy during the journey because you are too distracted from thinking about the time it takes to get there. It'll come.

To wrap this all up, you need to know what it takes to succeed in life, which you have already been equipped with. So, make the decision today to move in the right direction. Sis, we got you!

ABOUT THE AUTHOR

Tiffany Forte' is a Women's Fitness Specialist and owner of Fit and Female Fitness Program, Fit and Female Activewear, and Sweat the City Women's Fitness Summit. With a concentration in weight loss, strength gaining, pre/postnatal strength training, and running, she is passionate about encouraging conversations around mental health as it relates to fitness, diversity in the fitness space, and continuing to encourage black women and women of color to live healthier lifestyles.

Tiffany has found herself at the forefront of a movement to transform traditional fitness culture, with a specific focus on creating more spaces, experiences, and amplifying the voices for black women and women of color fitness enthusiasts to thrive, learn, and grow.

Since falling in love with fitness in 2012 and battling her own issues with food, weight, and mental health, Tiffany turned her passion for fitness into a thriving career in fitness entrepreneurship. Fit and Female is an uprising of black women, women of color, and anybody who feels like they don't "fit" in this space and who are committed to working to achieve your goals and striving to achieve the body and confidence you want – not what society pushes on you.

www.fitandfemale.net/
SOCIAL HANDLE: @iamfitandfemale

Your Story is Worth It
Tynitria Portis
Spiritual Leader and Confidence Coach

"Far greater things come to those who work hard. The journey is never easy, but it gets better."

For years, the staple of our existence has resided in who society deems we are. This conclusion is based on what our history is tied to, and we've just been trying to survive in the pain of what that story has created. We tend to discredit ourselves for something we're more than capable of. A life defined by who we are meant to be, with a fight in us that's resilient enough to make it worth living, instead of being caught up in the notion of constantly second-guessing ourselves. Measuring our worth by how big or important something or someone else is. Seeking externally for the approval of others when those opinions are formulated based on if that person believes they're enough or not.

Here's how that reality plays out in my mind.

I have this huge opportunity. Am I enough for it? Am I enough for this kind of success? Am I intelligent enough? What happens if I don't know enough?

I come from a rough past. Will I be accepted for who I am?

I want to impact and inspire many. Can I make that kind of difference in the world? Am I good enough?

It showed up when I decided to pour my heart into this project. As much as I believe that I am a good writer (and I am), I had no idea what I could contribute to *this* opportunity. It felt overwhelming to come up with a body of work of this magnitude even though I had written so many things on social media. Before I started writing, I prayed to God for help. He guided me through a spiritual transition of understanding where my worth lies before I could put one word down on paper. Finally, I understood how I had displaced my worth and what I needed to do to get it back and surrender it to Him.

I believe every experience we have begets a past reflection which is typically triggered by our pain. When you carry around the pain for so long, you either become...

1) **A prisoner of shame** - the person who takes all the blame or
2) **A victim** - the person who tends to blame everyone else.

We owe it to ourselves not to continue to allow ourselves to be consumed by our pain. Instead, let's take it as an opportunity to change the trajectory of our experiences by making a different choice. **The key to change is learning how to break free of the pain.** It may be hard, but you will reach a place of healing if you put in the work. Take it from someone who's come through her fair share of trials and tribulations. I can't tell you how often I've had to face that constant internal struggle of feeling like I am enough. Every prominent moment in my life has been a question of my worth riddled by being enough for it.

As you read the rest of this chapter, think about how you would answer each question. Then, as I share my personal experiences, pay close attention to any feelings or thoughts that may surface and allow yourself to feel into whatever comes up.

Are you worthy enough?
Growing up, all I wanted was to be happy. To achieve my idea of happiness, that meant I and everything else in my life had to be perfect. As optimistic as I wanted to be, the deep void nestled within the contents of my heart wouldn't allow me to feel into my joy. When you have a void that deep, it feels like a black hole that can never be filled no matter how hard you try, which is why I spent most of my life measuring my worth on a scale of who and what I could control, holding others to a certain standard so I wouldn't have to feel the pain. The beginning stages of my life were catalysts for the

battle I had with my worth. I never felt deserving of anything, so I always tried to prove myself. I was a good kid, smart, got good grades, and took on a lot at home as the oldest. I got tons of recognition and praise, but it still wasn't enough to fill the void. So, I did the next best thing, found something to place my value in, and attached myself to it. As a result of my childhood experiences, I played such a big part in taking care of my family, so I valued knowing they could depend on me. They needed me, and that's how I started defining my worth. You can be the one who carries the weight and burden of all the responsibilities, but what happens when it begins to take a toll on your mental and emotional well-being?

Do you let go or keep going?

I remember when I decided to let go of the responsibility for each one of my family members, one at a time, on every separate occasion. It's hard to say no without feeling guilty. It hurts to know someone is suffering because you chose not to help them. Even more so when you feel like you're the only one they can depend on, especially if your worth depends on it. The only way I could truly let go was by asking God for guidance. I still do. Every time someone asks me for anything. If He says no, I say no. It has taught me how to set boundaries and stand firm in them.

Here are a few things to consider when setting boundaries:
- Try not to sacrifice above your priorities.
- Try to help others who are trying to help themselves.
- If you urge to say no, go with your first mind.
- Most importantly, if/when you need to, seek guidance.

Here are a few benefits of honoring your boundaries:
- You get to keep your peace.
- It teaches others how to respect you.
- You build the confidence to say no without feeling guilty.
- You can put your time and energy into other important priorities.

Affirm: I am worthy enough to give up being the one who makes all the sacrifices to put myself first and make the important things a priority.

For those who decide to keep going, allow me to elaborate on what happens when you struggle to let go.

Are you strong enough?

My childhood experiences affected my ability to embrace being a mother. My adversity had all but prepared me for what it meant to have another human being solely depending on me. I was buried underneath my mother's absence and the pressure of my role as a mother to my siblings. Since I hadn't done anything specific to make a difference in dealing with my pain, I fell into a depression. Depression feels like you're walking around inside a hollow space filled with pain and anguish, wearing your anger as a protective covering with no way to escape. You feel like your life is no longer worth living and that you're not worth saving. When you feel like no one can save you, including yourself, how do you go on? Granted, some of us deal with depression much deeper and have to manage it as part of our daily living, **but God** … these are two of **THE** most powerful words for those of us who walk a life in faith.

God had my mom show up when I needed her the most in true divine intervention. I will never forget the way she spoke hope into my heart. The tears I cried that day had broken my spirit enough for me to make a conscious decision to carry my baby to term. I _packed_ up my feelings, moved in with my fiancé, and placed my value back into knowing that my family could depend on me. I couldn't give up. No matter what, it was never an option. If I wanted to be a good mom and a good wife (to be), I had to be perfect. As that pressure mounted up, I started to lose my sense of identity. I had built everything I was on being everything to everyone else, but I could no longer keep my frivolous idea of self-worth intact. It wasn't long before my mind drifted away from the image I had created. I wanted to be free with absolutely no way of knowing how I would get out. Finally, after years of emotionally detaching myself from my situation, I found my escape in the arms of another man.

My infidelity was and will always serve as a pivotal turning point in my life. Breaking someone's heart helped me realize my behavior's impact on myself and others. I hurt people without considering my part in it and used my broken past as a means to get away from the fact that **I was broken**. I was subconsciously leading myself down a path of self-destruction. I took all the blame, and that void got even deeper to the point where I had destroyed my worth. I know you're probably wondering how I got out of all of that.

I went to therapy which you'll read more about in the next section. Therapy helped me let go of my pain, and God helped me with my guilt. With both, I gained the knowledge and wisdom to forgive, trust and find the balance between having remorse and owning my part.

What does it mean to own your part?
- Having the ability to hold yourself in full accountability to a mistake or choice you've made with confidence.
- Being comfortable enough in your vulnerability to address, stand-in, and navigate conflict.

Here are a few things you can do to move into owning your part.
- Ask forgiveness, forgive others as well as yourself.
- Listen and try to understand every side of the story.
- Hold compassion for others and practice self-compassion for yourself.

Affirm: I am strong enough to let go and let God.

Letting go gives you the courage to win your battles without losing the fight.

Are you brave enough?
To salvage our relationship, we decided to go to therapy. Which meant I could no longer run from my problems; I had to deal with my pain and let go of my story from the past. **My story had always been about the little girl who was stuck with carrying her family on her own, trying to survive, and she could never ask for help because she had to be strong.** Doing it all by myself was no longer a viable option. If I wanted

to be enough of anything, accepting the help was my best bet. As much as I hated admitting to what I had done fully, I realized how important it is to speak up.

I have a voice.

What I have to say matters; how I feel matters, what I've been through, and what I'm going through issues. When you realize you matter, the void inside begins to fill up. Until this point, I had given my life to help others in a way that had depleted entirely every part of me. It wasn't long into therapy before we both realized that our time together had come to an end—this time, I chose to *pick* up my feelings and move forward with my healing. I had finally said yes to myself. A choice that brought me down a path of self-discovery into the core of my faith. God became the foundation of my self-worth.

Reflect on your own story.
- What is your story? What does it look like?
- How can you change or rewrite it?
- What support do you need?

Affirm: I am brave enough to ask for help.

You will notice that I had you affirm yourself throughout the chapter. Affirmations are vitally important because they reinforce belief in oneself. Words of Affirmation are one of my love languages, and for a long time, it was one of the standards I held others to. Now it is love that I give back to myself.

Every morning while brushing my teeth, I affirm with ...

I AM Worthy.
I AM Extremely Happy.
I AM Free from Me.
I AM Highly Valuable.
I AM Abundance.
I AM My Investment.
I AM My Very Best Investment.

This affirmation is followed by re-affirming that I am enough through God with an insert from Pastor Steven Furtick:

"Trust me enough to believe I am enough. Do you believe I am enough, and so are you? If I am in you and your God, I made you and put you in a situation. I will never put you in a situation that I will not make you enough for."

What becomes possible when you feel like you're enough?

For the first time in my life, I am married and spiritually aligned with someone in a way that's almost impossible to put into words. We live in a big beautiful two-story home that we purchased together for our first time amid a pandemic. I am working a successful corporate job while building a career as an entrepreneur. My nutrition is the foundation of my health, and I am more physically fit than I have ever been in my life. I am physically, emotionally, and mentally stable. I am a good mother, daughter, sister, and friend.

I am perfectly happy.

I am no longer a girl *fighting* to be happy.

I changed my story. **The pain is not the question. The pain is in answering the question and not knowing the answer.**

For the man and the woman who believes that your life is not worth it, I want you to know that …

No matter who you are.

No matter what you've been through.

No matter what you've done.

You Are Enough.

ABOUT THE AUTHOR

Tynitria is a Spiritual Leader and Confidence Coach who works with ambitious black men and women who struggle with feeling like they're enough. She helps her clients get out of the survival mentality, deal with their pain and let go of the story from the past so that they can live a life beyond what they thought was possible.

She is also the CEO and Founder of Insightful Beginning with Coach Tee, Certified Health and Life Coach with the Health Coach Institute, a Podcast Speaker, and soon to be Best Selling Author of her 1st Anthology! (Won't He Do It!)

www.insightfulbeginningwithcoachtee.com
Social Handle: @insightcoachtee

Your Journey is Worth It

Dr. LaQuista Erinna, DBH, LCSW

Licensed Psychotherapist and Wellness Coach

Imagine, after years of struggling to meet your goals, you finally reach a point in which you feel that you've "arrived." Things are going well in both your personal and business life. But unfortunately, the newfound feeling of success is when people usually get complacent and don't see the looming pitfalls of life. One lifelong lesson the military taught me was, 'to stay alert, is to stay alive.' The point is that you should always be aware of your surroundings and ready to pivot instantly.

So, after over 22 years in the Army, I should know better. At this stage in the game, we all know with life, the only thing that is certain and constant is ***change***. Yet I was, living my life out loud - married, mother, beautiful office to start my private practice, and I finally finished my doctorate. Things couldn't have been better - 'look, mama, I made it!' But I couldn't have been more wrong. Looking back, I realize that I became complacent. And that's why my divorce caught me off guard. This slippery slope led to a deep depressive state and the lowest point of my life. The myth of "The Strong Black Woman" told me that I would get through it unscathed. I would somehow be able to keep my business, care for my children, and do it with a smile. I would bounce back easily and quickly. Not necessarily because I was invincible, but because other people needed me. I was that one dependable person. So, if I was down and out, who would be there to help those who needed me? No one told me this, but it was how I felt about the role I played in the lives of my loved ones. So, I began to take on the notion that I had to be "strong" for others throughout my life. I would put on my cape and mask (hiding my pain) to save others, often at my determinant.

I figured that I could keep my business in New Jersey and travel from Georgia to see my clients bi-weekly. I would slowly transition existing clients to telehealth while setting up a new office space in Georgia. In the meantime, I could find a job. I was marketable, a licensed black psychotherapist in the Black Mecca of Atlanta. It would be "too easy" to find the perfect place to put my experience and education to work. I have my doctorate. I'm licensed. I'm smart. I'm at the top of my game. I got this! I had a plan in place. But little did I know, God had a much bigger plan for me, which I didn't understand at the time. We rarely do during a storm. But I now know that God was preparing me for everything to come.

Like many others, I lost a lot during the COVID-19 pandemic. I lost love, I lost money, and I lost my grandmother. I remember deciding what to feed my children at my lowest point for the week. My bank account was empty. As soon as any money would hit, it would be gone before I even noticed the deposit. I was too embarrassed to ask for help. I took my baby's piggy bank and went to one of the Coinstar machines to cash in what I could. After fees, I probably ended up with $200 to get groceries and pullups for the month. I would cry myself to sleep and refuse to answer any phone calls.

One day while I was in bed, I glance over at this $2,500 Peloton Bike that I had bought (on credit, remember I was broke-broke) and had only used twice in six months. Something just clicked for me at that moment. My mental and physical health was at an all-time low. My doctor was concerned about my stress level and increasing blood pressure. She started me on hypertension medication just a week prior. My therapist was worried about my mental stability and suggested I begin antidepressants. I raised many red flags for being at risk for suicide. Besides being diagnosed with major depressive disorder, post-traumatic stress disorder, and anxiety, I was grieving my marriage, experiencing financial distress, and overall felt hopeless. I could not see any positive way out of my current situation. I was labeled high-risk, and my doctor would call to assess for suicidality and safety. After one of those safety calls, I began to think of myself as one of my loved ones that I cared for so much. It was like an out-of-body experience. I could see myself telling myself that I had to take better care of myself. That was the beginning of my mindset shift to a healthier lifestyle and being Superwoman to save me.

Superwoman to Self-Care

You are caring. You are kind. You are loving. You are resilient. You are strong. You are honorable. You are responsible. You have probably used these phrases to describe a friend or loved one. It may be challenging to hear this, but these phrases also describe you. So many well-intended people use these phrases (or others) without realizing the gravity and weight. Superwoman is not a job one typically applies. Yet, so many women, especially Black women, find themselves in this role every day, from the stay-at-home mom who manages the household and everyone's schedule to the new work-from-home mom who juggles endless Zoom meetings and virtual learning. So many do it without complaints as if it's second nature, while most of us just push our frustration and overwhelm down because being Superwoman is the expectation. Superwomen care for others and often sacrifice themselves in the process. Even if you were a medical professional trying to save or comfort one of your patients, there's a beginning and end to your shift at some point. But when you're in your own life, caring for the people in your life can feel like a never-ending job. It's an additional duty that somehow, you become the "chosen one," and you accept it. In most cases, heroes happily provide care for others in their time of need, especially when it's a loved one.

Sometimes it is easy for nurturers to neglect their self-care and pour into others. By nature, you are always putting others before your own needs. While this speaks volumes to the type of person you are, you can easily and quickly experience "caregiver burnout" if you're not careful. The good news is all the qualities that make you an excellent nurturer and caregiver also mean you're fully capable of prioritizing yourself. You deserve to be always the best version of yourself. Look at it like this; you wouldn't want your loved one's nurse or doctor to work around the clock without a break, then must make essential decisions on their care. Right? Well, the same logic applies to you. Learning to implement coping skills, a support system, healthy boundaries, and a balanced routine will ensure that you operate in your gift and purpose at an optimum level. Self-care may feel overwhelming at first. You may not know how to make yourself a priority right now. So first things first, just stop and breathe.

Control: Breathe Life Back into Your Daily Routine by Mastering Breathwork

By now, we all agree that caring for others is often a high-stress and thankless job. Caring for yourself usually is an afterthought. It's important to develop coping tools to help combat feelings of overwhelm and burnout. Breathing is one of the first things all humans do. We do this automatically and instinctively. Understanding and implementing the power of breathwork is an essential practice for self-care. Breathwork is a foundational tool taught in many forms of therapeutic techniques. It may surprise you that this practice involves breathing exercises and includes focus and intention.

Four Square Breathing

Here's a technique I want you to try to get started.

Four Square or Box Breathing is a simple exercise that can help focus and ease anxiety.

1. Start by sitting comfortably with your back supported and feet on the ground. This position is essential because the support of your back against a chair or feet touching the floor will help you feel grounded. An alternate position is to sit on the floor, legs crossed, as if you are about to meditate. Remember to sit up straight, ensuring good posture.
2. When you're ready to begin the breathwork, start by slowly expelling the air from your lungs.
3. Next, breathe in through your nose for the count of four.
4. Now, hold your breath for the count of four.
5. Next, exhale slowly through your mouth for the count of four.
6. Finally, hold for the count of four.

This pattern continues as if you're creating a box or square. Four Square Breathing is a simple technique used in moments of high stress or as a part of your routine. As you get more comfortable with the exercise, you can increase your counts from four seconds to longer increments.

Using Movement to Reenergize Your Mind, Body, & Soul

You're physically and mentally strong, but the demands of being a Superwoman can take a toll. You may start to see your physical health deteriorate. There could be several reasons why the change occurs – excessive worry, putting off personal health needs to care for loved ones, financial strain, burnout, etc. The mental and emotional toll can lead to various emotions - sadness, empathy, anger, guilt, frustration, and everything in between.

We often see caregivers trying to manage their duties and day-to-day life along with anxiety and stress. It isn't until emotions start to physically manifest that people notice. Maybe your stomach feels like it's in knots, or you feel the sensation of butterflies. Severe prolonged stress and anxiety manifestations can lead to irritable bowel syndrome (IBS) or ulcers. Perhaps you carry stress and tension in your shoulders or back, leading to tense muscles and decreased range of motion or pain. Whatever the case, you want to focus on your breath until the feeling of any associated pain or discomfort is manageable before taking any further action.

For example, practice four square breathing until your stomach is no longer in knots or the intensity has changed. A great way to help the process along is movement.

Movement doesn't have to be in the traditional exercise like running, lifting weights, or push-ups. Instead, find something you enjoy doing—dancing, skating, hula hooping, etc. Just five or ten minutes of balancing a weighted hula hoop around your waist can be a fun way to get some moves in. Try adding some resistance bands to your thighs to turn up the intensity and get a great core workout. Going for a walk can be another great way to get out of the house and start moving. Thirty minutes of movement/exercise is preferable, but you can undoubtedly begin anywhere. If all you must give is 10 minutes, don't let that deter you from starting. You got this! Everything needed to take care of you is already inside of you. The tools provided here will help empower you to take control and reenergize your life.

Using Wellness Math to Find Purpose & Strength

You're capable of being well. Wellness is often associated with diet, exercise, mental health, or maybe even the chemicals we use in our home. These components are a part of wellness, but let's dig deeper by adding the people around you. "People" include family, friends, lovers, associates, strangers, etc. Take a moment to evaluate all the closest relationships to you. Now ask yourself the following questions and record your response:

Who? Who are the people that are closest to you?

_____

_____

_____

_____

_____

_____

_____

_____

What? What value do they add to your life? Or do they take a lot more than they add?

_____

_____

_____

_____

_____

_____

_____

_____

When? When was the last time they showed up for you? I mean, they really showed up for you when you needed them. Have they asked if you needed a break? Have they noticed that you're not yourself and checked in to ensure you are okay?

_____

_____

_____

_____

_____

_____

_____

_____

_____

_____

Why? Why are these relationships important to you? Why is it essential to the other person? Do you find that the relationship is one-sided?

_____

_____

_____

_____

_____

_____

_____

_____

_____

_____

How? How are your boundaries with them? Are they healthy? We have the most challenging time setting healthy boundaries with family and friends. It is essential to have people around you who add value to your life. Gentle reminder: You **DO NOT** owe anyone access to you because they are your mother, father, sibling, best friend, or lover.

_____

_____

_____

_____

_____

_____

_____

_____

_____

_____

You may have heard of "the butterfly effect." If not, this is the belief that small changes can drastically impact the more extensive system in the future. While this theory of chaos does not entirely apply to self-care, we can draw a few connections. First, it is true; you cannot take care of others if you don't care for yourself. Now imagine taking care of your loved one for years with little assistance. Your daily routine entirely revolves around your loved one's schedule, leaving little to no time for yourself. This process is not sustainable. Now imagine that you implement one small change such as working out (fitness), attending therapy (mental health), or changing to a healthier diet (wellness). Just one small change in the equation can drastically affect your overall quality of life in the future. **Fitness + Mental Health + Wellness = Mindset Shifts** is an excellent formula to keep in mind. Your mindset will be one of your best indications of meaningful change. Remember that you are capable of wellness, and you deserve it. Start subtracting some harmful elements and adding more positives to your life and routine. You will notice the effects of a more balanced and less stressed life. When you take care of yourself, it shows. By implementing a fitness routine, taking care of my mental health, and focusing on wellness, I created a mindset that my life matters. This shift from being Superwoman to a Self-Care (ER) is so fundamentally crucial to my life and those around me that I love the most.

Finally, look at the 10 Affirmations of A Self-Care (ER). Write them down, take a picture or screenshot of them and place them somewhere you can see them daily on your mirror or wallpaper on your phone. Then, say them aloud daily and repeatedly. Say them until you start implementing them and believe them to be true.

10 Affirmations of A Self-Care (ER)

Because Self-Care is Urgent-Care

1. I love myself.
2. I trust that I can care for myself.
3. I shall prioritize both my physical and mental health.
4. I can be kind to others without sacrificing my own needs.
5. I know how to advocate for myself and my needs.
6. I listen to and trust my instincts.
7. I set and stick to healthy boundaries.
8. I will forgive myself when I make mistakes.
9. I will be fully present in the moment.
10. I will ask for help when needed.

ABOUT THE AUTHOR

Dr. LaQuista is a licensed psychotherapist and wellness coach. She created well + fit living™ after recognizing many of her clients, particularly women, struggled with self-care. The brand includes a monthly subscription box, card deck, planner, and other items to help anyone seeking help on their self-care journey.

www.wellfitliving.com
SOCIAL HANDLE: @laquistaerinna

Your Grief is Worth it
Christine Greene
Licensed Practical Nurse and Personal Trainer

I truly believe the loved ones we lose in death are still loved and walk beside us daily. We hold on to the love we once had and cherish the memories we created. However, I recently learned the excruciating fact that losing a parent in death is extremely hard. For me, the guilt and depression hit me like a ton of bricks. The guilt hit me with all the "if only I had asked more questions" or "if only I had said no to the procedure," she would still be here. The pain I felt from losing my mom was unbearable.

I couldn't sleep, I couldn't eat, sometimes it took all I had to breathe. The day my mom passed, I felt like the wind had been knocked out of me when the Dr. said, "she's gone." I was in disbelief. All I could do was cry and scream. My world had been shattered into pieces. Then came the immeasurable anger. Reality set in very quickly. I was numb. The denial was real for me. I couldn't accept that my mom was gone. I could not wrap my mind around the fact that my mom was never coming back. How do I live without her? How do I go on in life and not have her by my side? Soon after her memorial services were over, I had to pick up the pieces and put life back together without her. How was I going to get through life without my best friend? When I need advice, who am I going to call now? How do I begin to cope with her death? These questions alone were overwhelming as I processed my new norm without her.

The return to work was tough. I was used to talking to my mom every day before going to work. Most mornings, I would go to her house and check on her. We would have our morning chats and breakfast dates. This norm was horrible without her. Life for me felt like it was ending. The weeks progressed, and life continued. The holiday season was right around the corner. It was our first Thanksgiving and Christmas without her. My now-husband proposed to me on Christmas Day that year. The experience it was bitter-sweet. I was sad because my mom wasn't there at that moment. At the same time, I was overjoyed that I was engaged to the love of my life. But then I felt guilty that I had a moment of happiness. But in my heart, I knew my mom would want me to live in the moment and embrace my happiness. Less than five days later, we found out we were expecting. That was a total shock to us. My husband and I were super excited. But once again, I was sad because she wasn't here to share these moments with me.

Once I found out I was pregnant, I immediately suppressed my grief. I refused to cry. I was determined to be as happy as possible during my pregnancy. I wanted a happy and healthy baby. Yet, I was suffering in silence. I had a void that couldn't be filled. Nevertheless, I had to push through it. I had to nurture and love the baby growing inside of me. My older son was having a hard time processing my mom's death. So, I sought out professional help for him. He did well with counseling. As for myself, I had mixed feelings about seeking out professional help initially. So, I put the idea of counseling on the back burner. My thought process was if I keep myself distracted, I won't think about it. He would get the help he needed, but I was to push through.

Within a couple of weeks after having my daughter, postpartum postpartum depression came full force with a vengeance!!!! Depression plus grief was all too much for me!!! I cried all the time as I held my baby close to my heart. I just wanted to pick up the phone and call my mom, and I couldn't. I wanted her to meet her granddaughter and bond with her, but I knew that wasn't possible. My emotions were up and down like a roller coaster. It was up and down constantly. It was draining and very lonely. I tried not to always talk about my feelings as I didn't want to burden anyone with my sorrows. I soon felt the effects of not talking about how I felt. Little did I know it was like a ticking time bomb just waiting to explode. It was only a matter of time. As a nurse, the guilt of my mother's death haunted me. I felt as if I had let her down. I didn't protect her. The day she passed kept replaying over and over in my mind. It was torturing me. I started to turn to food as a source of comfort. My nutrition was nonexistent.

I gained back the weight I had lost from having my daughter. I had surrendered to grief and depression. Before long, I noticed other changes that took place. I was irritable all the time. I was unhappy with the woman I saw in the mirror. I knew I needed help. After talking to my husband, sister, and best friend, I knew I had to do something different. I was becoming a person that I did not like. I was not the woman that my mother raised me to be. I took a good look in the mirror and decided that it was time to change my thoughts and take control of my mental health. I finally worked up the courage to seek out a therapist.

The first therapist and I didn't connect. At first, I was upset that she wasn't the right therapist for me. I let that discourage me from seeking help because I was new; I didn't realize that finding the right therapist and building a trusting relationship was a process. We talked about this as a family and not something we openly talked about in my community. A few months went by before I sought out help again. Finally, my current therapist was recommended to me through a good friend. After the first session, I felt some relief. I felt less pressure from my guilt. My therapist made me feel comfortable. My therapist created a safe space for me to feel comfortable, and I was able to open to her and pour my heart out. Gradually after each session, I started to feel better. I slowly began to regain power over my thoughts and feelings. I began to acknowledge that my thoughts and feelings were worth sharing and not suppressing.

As time went on, I was ready to take back my health. No doubt it has been a struggle to lose weight. I wanted to lose weight, but at the same time, I wasn't motivated to take the necessary steps. Finally, one of my clients contacted me about training her at the gym. I was excited, and I quickly said yes. This is just what I needed. It was time for me to get back to my passion for health and wellness. As a trained health professional, I love to help people improve their health. I told myself that I needed to love myself and allow myself to feel better. I was getting back to the lifestyle I once knew of being healthy and active. It's been a struggle. I've started and stopped many times throughout my health journey. One of the best feelings to experience during exercise is the release of endorphins, the body's feel-good chemical. I am truly in my happy space when exercising and training my clients. For me, exercise has been the best anti-depressant when I stick with it. I always feel better after a good workout. My mind is free and clear when I am working out. Yet, to this day, I struggle with consistency and staying motivated. My journey is my journey. So, I don't have to put unnecessary pressure on myself. I must keep going. In my mind, I can hear my mom telling me, "You may get tired and slow down, but you must not quit!" As I go through my journey, I reflect on the last three years. I am not where I want to be; however, I appreciate that I am not where I used to be. I have some clarity about myself and my goals. I am working on becoming a better version of myself. This allows me to challenge myself and create a judgment-free space for myself and others. My therapist has encouraged me to journal my thoughts and feelings on paper. At first, I didn't think it would be helpful. As it turned out, it was therapeutic for me. I was able to express my feelings on paper, and the best part of all.... my journal is judgment-free. I can express myself the way I need to, not holding back my feelings. I am free to be me when I express my thoughts. I do not have to apologize for how I feel; I am unapologetically free to be in my journal.

Here are my takeaways to know that your emotions are worth it:
1. Honor your grief and your emotions (don't suppress them express them)
2. Share your feelings with your partner and friends (even if they can't make you feel better, you won't feel alone)
3. Seek professional help (know that starting a new relationship takes time)
4.   Get back to some normalcy (take it one day at a time.... baby steps)
5. Get strong in your body so you can feel good in your mind (working out releases endorphins that make you feel good)

I have learned I am worth it throughout this entire process, and my life is worth it.

I will tell you; Your Life Is Worth It! Your Life Is Worth It! You Are Worth It!!!

ABOUT THE AUTHOR

Christine Green is a Licensed Practical Nurse and Personal Trainer. She is the founder of G&G Fitness and Nutrition. Christine is on a mission is to help clients live a healthy and active lifestyle.

SOCIAL HANDLE: @gngfitnessnnutrtion

Your Bliss is Worth it
Leslie M. Atley
National Board Certified Health and Wellness Coach

After 44 years of trying to figure out and control the outcomes, I decided I would take a leap of faith and be ok with not having all the answers. So, I decided to take the cape off and BE. It was scary and uncomfortable, but the most amazing thing happened after I got comfortable being uncomfortable. I have found myself blown away by an abundance of perpetual blessings in my life. Whether it is the multiple open doors and opportunities, the growth of my business, making memories with my family, or living the life I dreamed about, I am finally experiencing the fulfillment that I had only read about. Bliss that I didn't believe was meant for me. As I give thanks for my life of fulfillment and bliss, the spirit reminds me that I am worthy of this life, and so are you.

When you think of health and wellness, what do you think of? Most people think health and wellness are predicated by diet, exercise, and lack of disease. I was most people up until a couple of years ago. I thought my wellness was measured by my weight, diet, exercise, and drinking plenty of water. While the aforementioned are important proponents of the health and wellness formula, optimal health and wellness (a holistic approach) include bliss and fulfillment. As a national board-certified health and wellness coach, I want to encourage, empower, and equip you to expand your health and wellness goals this year to include bliss and fulfillment. Your body, emotions, mind, and spirit will thank you.

What is Bliss?

Going about our day, we experience people, places, and things that make us happy. Happiness comes from external influences. It is temporary; as such, we always pursue happiness. Joy is internal and connected to our identity. No matter what is going on in our life, we can still choose joy. Joy and happiness are emotions we experience daily. However, to experience bliss, we must dive deeper into our conscious and subconscious minds and embrace the truth of our existence and identity. Bliss is a conscious state of being. It's a place of being whole, complete, and connected to our purpose on earth. Bliss is there for us to experience whether we acknowledge it or not. We embody bliss when our body aligns with our emotions, and our emotions align with our mind, and our mind aligns with our spirit's remembrance that we were designed to live a life of bliss. You are worthy of bliss.

What is Fulfillment?

Wikipedia defines fulfillment as satisfaction or happiness because of fully developing one's abilities or character, the gratification of desire, especially in dreams. Like bliss, fulfillment is connected to our identity and aligning our body, emotions, mind, and spirit with the truth of our being (abilities and character). To live a fulfilled life, we must release our limiting beliefs, self-doubt, and the spirit of inferiority imposed on us many generations ago. We are fulfilled by design. We live a life of fulfillment by intentionally mastering ourselves and knowing our dreams (big and small) are destined to be our reality. Mastering self requires us to know, believe, and speak the truth of who we are, the power we possess, and our ability to be our best self. Our dreams are not meant to be deferred. Our dreams are intended to give us a vision of what is possible, a foreshadowing of a possible future, a glimpse into our heart's desires. Fulfillment comes when our self-mastery opens the door to manifesting dream after dream after dream. It's not one and done; it's a continuum. You are worthy of fulfillment.

How Do Bliss and Fulfillment Affect My Health and Wellness?

Let's imagine that our health and wellness are impacted by our spirit, mind, emotion, and body in that order.

Spirit- The foundation of bliss and fulfillment is found in the spirit. We cannot experience bliss or fulfillment without connecting to our spirit/source/higher being. Spirit is truth, and our identity and dreams come from truth. Our daily practice of connecting to spirit allows us to see ourselves divinely, whole, healthy, and light-filled. Spirit guides our actions toward a healthy mind, emotional state, and body. We cannot be healthy or well if we are ill in spirit.

Mind- Our visions and dreams reside in the mind along with our thoughts, beliefs, and understanding. We think, believe, and know to be true either manifest the dreams and visions or kill them. A healthy mind results from self-mastery practices like meditation, affirmations, positive thinking, seeking truth, knowledge, and understanding. Fulfillment shapes our mental health by generating thoughts, beliefs, and wisdom that align with the truth of our being and capabilities.

Emotion- Low vibrational emotions like fear, anger, worry, and doubt contribute to illness in the body and mind. The highest emotion we can experience is bliss. In this state, our body and mind perform optimally. Bliss is a state of being where our organs are the healthiest and our body systems function at a high level. The emotion of bliss prevents and heals disease in the body and regulates the mind's thoughts and mental health.

Body- Disease results from lack of ease in the body (dis-ease). Bliss and Fulfillment support flow and homeostasis in the body. The way we take care of our vessels indicates our self-mastery, spiritual practices, and mental and emotional states. Eating a healthy diet, exercising regularly, drinking water, and managing stress are keys to managing disease and living a blissful and fulfilling life.

8 Steps to Bliss/Fulfillment- Staying in S.H.A.P.E with LMA

I manifested a life of bliss and fulfillment by staying in S.H.A.P.E with LMA. Before staying in SHAPE, I had to master loving me always (LMA). Every day, minute, and second, I am intentional about loving ME. I had to learn that I was worthy of loving me, ALL of ME (the good, the bad, and the ugly). When I feel out of sorts or dis-ease, I know there is some area of my life lacking love. My body, emotions, mind, and spirit all function at their best when I practice self-love. There is no bliss or fulfillment without self-love. In addition to self-love, I decided to practice radical self-care centered around putting ME FIRST EVERYDAY UNAPOLOGETICALLY. If I am last on my to-do list, I am not fulfilled. It took 44 years for me to figure that out. But with my fulfillment came my bliss, and I've never known love or life like this, and I am worth it! Fulfillment and Bliss are my birthrights, and they are yours too. Now let's stay in S.H.A.P.E with LMA.

1. **Speak what you want** - So many times, we speak things as they currently are in life or our current situation or even the gloom and doom that we see coming. Now is the time to posture and position yourself to speak what you want. God is faithful and able to do exceedingly and abundantly above everything we could ask or think, so speak, what you want. Speak those things that are deep down in your soul, the things you've never told anybody because you weren't sure if you were worthy of it. Turn up your faith, speak what you want, and know that you can have what you want. I started teaching virtually for Legacy Holistic Health Institute in 2019. My virtual background was always water and the beach. My students would ask, "why is that your background? Are you going there?" My response was, I'm trying to manifest that I will teach from a place like this one day. August 2021, I experienced bliss and fulfillment as I taught my class from Cabo, with the beautiful ocean and beach as my background. I spoke it into existence in 2019. Know that you can speak what you want into existence too. Don't be scared; turn up your faith and speak what you want. You are worthy of the desires of your heart, so speak life. Start a journal of your wants. *Write affirmations in the future tense for everything you desire and speak them daily when you wake up and before you go to bed. When you manifest what you've been affirming, add something else and affirm it.* There is no limit to what you can have.

2. **Happy (Choose to BE)** - It's time to be happy and healthy. You may ask, how do I do that? Choose it! When you wake up, command your morning, and decide I will be happy today. Speak it and do the things you need to do to be happy. For example, if you're experiencing something that brings you down or causes your depression, you might need to turn the TV off, you might need to meditate more on God's word, or meditate on what you're grateful for. When you take a moment to focus on what you're grateful for, it will bring you joy. Be

optimistic, Be positive, Be confident, Be loving, Be free, Be bold…. Laugh often. Smile, it's contagious. You are worthy of joy and happiness as you journey toward bliss.

3. **Healthy (Choose to BE)** -Tap into what you need to do to be healthy. You may need to change a little bit of what you eat. You may need to move your body a little bit more. You may need to start changing what you're taking into your ear and eye gates. Check your heart. The best way to take care of your heart is by reducing your stress and moving the body. Being healthy is a choice. You must choose to drink more water. You must choose to eat more fruits and vegetables. You must choose to move your body. A few months ago, while on vacation, I came upon a horrendous flight of steps. My first thought was, let me find the elevator. My health coach (yes, the health coach has a health coach) said, "no, just take it one step at a time." So, I chose to move beyond my limiting thoughts and beliefs and move my body up all those steps. Once I got to the top, I was out of breath, but I also felt proud and fulfilled. You may feel like you can't do it for your health goals; get yourself a coach like I did who can support, encourage, and guide you. Choose to be healthy every day and experience fulfillment every step of the way. You are worthy of good health and long life.

4. **Align**- This is the season for us to align with the people, places, and things that match up with our truth and our being. Be who you are authentically. If you say I'm a traveler, then be ready to get on the plane when somebody gives you an invitation for an all-expense-paid trip. If you say I am a believer, show it by exercising your faith and showing the peace and grace of God everywhere you go. Align with who you truly are. Align with your values and what is important to you. Align with God, your truth, and your purpose. Alignment brings you bliss and the overwhelming feeling of fulfillment you are worthy of.

5. **Ascend** - After alignment comes ascension. Ascension is a continuous rise up. There is no final destination. As you grow and level up, you will continue to elevate to new heights. With growth and expansion, there is always more to do.

If you find yourself stagnant, complacent, or stuck, know that you are not growing, and it's time to go up a little higher.

There is nothing wrong with ascension. People may say, "what are you doing now? Where are you going?" Be confident that this is your time of ascension. Some people will go with you; some people will not. Don't let them stop you. God will make provision for you to go higher and higher, from glory to glory and mountain top to mountain top, until you reach the pinnacle of your existence. Don't be afraid you were created for this, and everything you need is already in you. You are worthy of every high place, elevation, and promotion you receive/achieve.

6. **Protect Your Peace** - We live in a time where everything that is going on in the world can rob, steal, and kill our peace, so we must protect our peace. Surround yourself with people who bring you peace, not chaos. Start your mornings by doing the things that put your mind, body, and spirit in a peaceful state. That might be prayer, meditation, reading, burning a candle, doing yoga. No matter what it is, protect your peace at all costs and guard your heart. Be mindful and present for the things that matter most. You are worthy of peace that surpasses all understanding.

7. **Prosper** -We will naturally prosper when we protect our peace and ascend. Not just financially. We will prosper in peace. We will prosper in momentum. We will prosper in relationships and connections. We will prosper in what we say and how we think. We will prosper in every area of our lives without guilt. Bliss, fulfillment, and prosperity go hand in hand. You are sitting underneath open heaven, be open to every blessing with your name on it. Have an attitude of gratitude and a heart to give from your overflow, and you will lack no good thing. You are worthy of a prosperous life.

8. **Expect Excellence** - Wake up every day, expecting excellence to show up in every area of your life. You will not be disappointed. Expect excellent unexpected blessings. Expect that things will work out excellently. Expect

excellence in everything you put your mind, heart, and hands to do. Expect excellence from the people who come into your circle. Expect excellent opportunities. Expect excellent connections. Expect excellent answers to your prayers. Expect excellent doors to open. Expect excellence in your health. Expect excellence in your business/on your job. Expect excellence in your home. Expect excellence to flow to you and from you. By faith, know that you are worthy of the excellence and the blessings that God has with our name on it. Expect it, and it will come.

Staying in SHAPE is how I maintain a life of health and wellness through bliss and fulfillment. You, too, can experience next-level health and wellness by practicing these eight simple steps:

- ✓ **Speak** what you want.
- ✓ Choose to be **Happy** and **Healthy.**
- ✓ **Align** and **Ascend.**
- ✓ **Protect** your **Peace** and **Prosper.**
- ✓ **Expect Excellence**.

S.H.A.P.E is more than food and exercise.
It's a holistic approach to loving yourself to wellness.

Some tools to support your journey to Bliss/Fulfillment
- Aromatherapy - I started using a diffuser with essential oils every night and morning. I chose the oils based on what I felt I needed. My favorites are rose, patchouli, lavender, eucalyptus, and frankincense. I also started burning incense and candles of different fragrances and characteristics related to what I was doing or needed for the day.
- Crystals- I learned the properties of different crystals and used them in my healing journey. My favorites are rose quartz, tiger's eye, aventurine, amethyst, and crystal quartz.
- Books- As an adult, I've always loved to read. At any given time, I may be reading 3-4 books. Leaders read.

- Affirmations- I use post-it notes to write my affirmations and put them in my mirror for daily reflection.
- Hot Tea- A cup of hot tea during my one-on-one time with God is serene, calming, and peace-filled.
- Music- I have come to love music. I enjoy turning my favorite song up in the car and singing and dancing like nobody's watching.
- Dancing- I don't particularly enjoy exercise, but dancing has become my favorite way to get moving and be free.
- Laughter- I recognize my laughter is my most significant asset, and I often laugh to keep from crying. I am intentional about laughing every day, even if I must laugh at myself.
- Sisterhood- whether I am spending time with the Tillie Girlz, Soul Wealth Sisters, My College BFFs, My Looking Out the Window Crew, My Legacy Family, or Random Sisters, God sends my way, the time, love, experiences, testimonies, and laughter we share reflects my love for ME.
- Prayer, Meditation, and Journaling- My one-on-one time with the one who loved me first and continues to love me best is the most important part of my day. It doesn't look the same every day. Some days I am on my knees in prayer, somedays I am sitting by the ocean as the sun rises; some days, I must sit still and write what the spirit speaks to me. However, it happens. I know there is no greater LOVE!

ABOUT THE AUTHOR

Leslie M. Atley is a two-time author and health and wellness expert with 20+ years of experience in health promotion and prevention. She shares her experience and expertise in various roles such as National Board Certified-Health and Wellness Coach, Legacy Holistic Health Institute and VA Whole Health Faculty. As the Lead Health Coach and owner of Loving Me Always, LLC, Leslie offers international holistic (mind, body and spirit) health coaching services and disease prevention trainings and workshops. LMA's slogan is Me First Everyday Unapologetically. Leslie is committed to informing, teaching, supporting, and shifting women to loving themselves to wellness and a life of bliss.

www.lovingmealways.com
SOCIAL HANDLE: @lma_lovingmealways

Your Destiny is Worth It
Clarissa Pritchett
Certified Integrative Nutrition Health Coach

Girl, your life is worth it! Yes, I am talking to the beautiful woman who decided to pick up this book and take the time to read it. I am also talking to myself as I remember when I did not believe my life was not worth anything outside of the lies I was told and believed. If you are reading this chapter and by God would have it, you grew up like me; then you know what it means not to think your life was worth much at all. I could not see past my environment or outside the family dynamic I was born into, which was very unhealthy. I grew up in a small town and in a single-parent home as a minority during a time there was no internet, minimal resources, or anyone to pour healthy wisdom into me.

I grew up feeling that I was not good enough, smart enough, tall enough, a light or dark "skin" enough, pretty enough, and name all the other inadequacies out there "enough." As a young child, I did not know what it meant to be spiritually, emotionally, physically, mentally, or emotionally healthy. Spiritually, I questioned God about my life purpose. I did not have adults speaking life into me or encouraging me to grow up and be or do great things in my life. My flaws were constantly being pointed out. Family members, peers, and even a teacher told me that I would not amount to anything in life. I could not see a bigger purpose for my life outside of my surroundings and believed having a good life was meant for those born into a home with two parents with money.

Physically, I was overweight as a child. My physical activity consisted of walking to and from school and cleaning our small apartment before my mom came home from work. When I didn't complete my chores, my discipline was physical. If you have ever seen the videos on social media about "Growing Up Hispanic," you surely know what I am talking about. Sitting down to watch TV and relax was unheard of, and if I was caught sitting around, I was told I was lazy. Leisure time was hidden, and guilt sunk in afterward. Also, I didn't physically know how to "look like a girl" and dressed like a tomboy up until high school. I had no physical pride or confidence in myself as a young lady. I was not taught to comb my hair or put on makeup. There were no "YouTube" tutorials for me to watch, so I admired other young girls my age that looked put together and wondered if they had someone teaching them to be girly.

Mentally, since a very young age, my mind wondered why my father committed suicide when I was three days old in front of my mom. I was bullied at school and called "the girl who'd dad killed himself" and told by classmates that my dad killed himself because I was an ugly baby and he did not want me. My mind was consumed with the violence at home and being bullied at school. I lived in constant fear and stayed in fight or flight mode. I did not have dreams to grow up and be something amazing because I didn't think or believe it was possible. Emotionally, I ate my feelings from a very young age. I remember eating bowls of cereal and milk topped with a cup of sugar. When I finished my cereal, I would mix the milk and sugar and drink it down. Next, I would stuff my mouth with traditional Hispanic plates filled with rice, beans, tacos, tostadas, and enchiladas. Knowing what I know now as a health coach, I would eat until I was in a food coma as a kid and go to sleep in my feelings too.

In addition to eating my emotions, I would "stuff down" how I felt because the discussion of feelings didn't happen in our family. Stuffing down my feelings resulted in bouts of anger in my early teen years and resulted in me being a "problem student" who stirred up strife in the streets and school. I remember hating life and feeling like I would wake up to walk around day after day haphazardly. Thankfully, one pivotal moment when I was sent to the principal's office in seventh grade for cursing out a teacher, I remember crying out to God in my mind and thinking, "God, if you are real, please show me that you are there and what the purpose of my life is." And that day was actually the first day I had someone speak life into me. I will never forget how the principal looked at me and said, "one day, you will be a teacher and help a lot of people."

That was the answered prayer I needed! But it was a lot of emotions for my pre-teen mind to absorb.

Nevertheless, deep down, I knew I needed to water that seed planted in my mind that day. That afternoon, I discovered a bible underneath the couch when I got home. I want to say I read passages for almost an hour as tears rolled down my face. I went back and forth in my mind and thought about what my principal had said. I also doubted what he said and wondered how that would ever be possible for me. I also remember one of the passages I read in Romans 12:2, "be transformed by the renewing of your mind," and it was like God was speaking to me, letting me know for my life to be different, my mind needed to be different. Every day after that, I would go home to do my chores, and I would secretly pull out that bible and read it. I decided that I needed to change despite what was happening around me. I started praying and asking God for hope and signs for a better life.

The next pivotal moment for me was taking health education as an elective class the following year. Everything in my textbook was fascinating, and I wanted to try to implement everything that I was reading. Living in a low-income single-parent home was another challenge, but I started making small changes like going to the salad bar at lunch instead of the regular lunch line. My food choices were limited at home, but I started eating smaller portions and noticing when I wanted to stress eat. My next "Ahh Ha" moment was when I was sitting on the couch eating tacos for dinner, and an infomercial came on with Billy Blanks promoting Tae Bo workout videos. I vividly remember putting my plate down on the floor and thinking to myself, "That's it! That is what I want to do!" I wanted to be like the Billy Blanks Tae Bo infomercial women looking fit and helping others. I also remember Billy Blanks talking about mindset in the commercial and conquering harmful self-talk to get through the workouts and get healthy. I knew I had to find a way to get those Tae Bo VHS tapes. I cleaned houses on the weekends to help my mom and to make extra money on the side. That very weekend I asked the older man I worked for to order the Tae Bo videos instead of paying me. Thankfully, he ordered the VHS tapes and paid me too! When the videos arrived, I was ecstatic. I then started a routine into the ninth grade where I would get home as fast as I could, do my chores, read a scripture, and get my Tae Bo workout in before my mom got home. Those videos planted the next seed in me to change my mindset and believe my life and health were worth more!

I remember other peers my age talking about sports, dating, and doing fun things outside of school. I would get invited to hang out and decline because I had responsibilities and had grown to love the routine I started daily after school. Doing things outside the norm of my environment and what my peers were doing made me uncomfortable. I had left the unhealthy crowds of friends and family members I once surrounded myself with, and I wondered if the changes I was making would make a difference. I wondered if what I was doing after school and on the weekends would help me become a teacher to make a difference for others one day. I did have those so-called friends and family members tell me I was starting to act like I was better than them and made fun of me for not wanting to hang out with them anymore. I battled with thoughts, like "who do you think you are?" and "you will never be enough," but going home to read and workout gave me a sense of purpose...looking back, working out, and reading scriptures was feeding my mind and my soul even though I was doing it in secret.

Fast forward to high school; I had my eyes set on joining the military and getting as far away as possible to make a new life for myself. Finally, all the Tae Bo workouts and scriptures did start to pay off. Although I did not have the family support I wished I had, I had worked my way to becoming senior class president and graduated in the top ten percent of my class. However, I still had to work hard on canceling out the noise of doubt and negative opinions of others that liked to remind me of my early adolescent years. I repeated Billy Blanks motivational quotes to myself every day unknowingly; they were my affirmations at the time.

Here are just a few:
- "Mindset is everything!"
- "If you believe you can, you will!
- "Where I am today is where my mind is and will put me; where I am tomorrow is where my mind will put me!"
- "A strong mind can overcome anything!"

In addition to Billy Blanks having a positive impact on my life at a young age, I also want to share that I started reading books from the library from the "Self-Help" section. I would rush in and out of the library very quickly, grabbing books so nobody would see me. I can say I put more effort into reading those books than my English books. I became fascinated with Myles Monroe and his books about unlimited potential. Those books kept me going and looking back; I thank God for every struggle I went through as a child. It became apparent why I had to go through what I went through. Suppose I would have grown up with things handed to me; I may not be where I am today. I am an Army Medical Officer, Speaker, Author, and Coach with a mindset that I still have more to learn spiritually, emotionally, physically, mentally, and emotionally. I must improve my life because I am worth it. I am letting you know your life is worth it too!

I want to encourage you to hold on to those struggling, tired, or ready to give up no matter your age. You will be a teacher and someone helping others with your story. The darkness and the pain are temporary. I know it is difficult, but it's not impossible. If God can turn my life around while being a child in the 1990s with the bible, Billy Blanks VHS tapes, and self-help books, he can change your life in the twenty-first century with much more available to you! Society will tell us our self, and life worth depends on always being confident; constantly feeling capable; always comfortable in our skin; always feeling worthy and always doing everything and overwhelming ourselves to feel accomplished.

But self and life worth are:

1, Being honest with your thoughts, struggles, and emotions
2. Defining what living healthy and well means to you
3. Internal and personal development without pressure from the world
4. Loving yourself without the approval of others
5. Forgiving yourself and others and
6. Getting back up as many times as we need to get up.
7. Speaking life into our past, present, and future self

ABOUT THE AUTHOR

Clarissa Pritchett, M.P.H., is an Integrative Nutrition Health Coach, Empowerment Speaker, Author, Entrepreneur, and Army Medical Service Corps Officer. Clarissa is a wife and mom to three beautiful boys. Clarissa is passionate about health and wellness and has served numerous clients over the past 20 years. She has a Bachelor's degree in Health Education, a Master's Degree in Public Health Nutrition and numerous certifications in the fitness and nutrition field. She is an online health coach and self-care coach who also mentors women to start online businesses while promoting Sisterhood, Self-Care, and Service to those in need. She loves to encircle and uplift women to live healthy lives. She has written numerous recipe and health guide eBooks. She is a sought after speaker and resilience instructor for the military, wellness companies, and local churches to where she shares her story of overcoming health/life challenges and motivates women with their health and life goals. Clarissa is a short, sweet, and spicy mixed salad sistah that keeps it real, raw, and organic about how she overcame many health challenges and body issues. Overall, her favorite things in life are Jesus, family, friends, cooking and eating food, especially tacos, donuts, and chocolate!

www.clarissapritchett.com

SOCIAL HANDLE: @ClarissaHealthCoach

Your Authentic Power is Worth It
Christine Ramsay
Certified Diversity Professional
Happiness and Leadership Coach

I remember starting a new school and feeling nervous about my first day when I was young. I remember walking into my new school, hoping to make some new friends on my first day. What kept me super anxious throughout the day wasn't about finding my classrooms or meeting my teachers. It was who I was going to sit with at lunch. This thought was on auto-repeat in my mind throughout the day. The bell finally rang for lunch, which felt like days versus a few hours, and there I was, walking towards the cafeteria with my lunch bag in hand. I could feel my heart beating faster and faster as I approached the cafeteria. I walked in, and I immediately felt a sigh of relief when I could see an open table with a few girls already sitting there. I walked a bit faster, hoping the spot would still be available, and thankfully I made it. I plotted down next to them, giving them a shy smile.

I just about convinced myself to have the bravery of opening a conversation with the girls until I opened my lunch bag, and there it was, the food that my dear Armenian grandmother had packed for me. Unfortunately, it was filled with delicious but super smelly Armenian food like garlic hummus and Armenian pizza, which had a distinct and unpleasant odor. Suddenly, I heard the girls giggling and holding their noses with their faces looking with disgust as they ran to sit at a different table away from me. My utter nightmare came true, sitting alone in the big cafeteria on my first day and feeling like I didn't belong. I came home in tears, and the first thing I said to my grandmother was never again to pack me Armenian food for lunch. I told her I wanted to be like everyone else and pack peanut butter/jelly sandwiches or deli sandwiches and nothing different! I wanted to feel connected to others and feel like I belonged, even if it meant hiding my own cultural identity—which I truly valued and what I authentically enjoyed. But, like most kids my age, I was willing to put all that aside just to fit in.

I realized that my uniqueness was my real advantage as I grew up. I had this solid cultural upbringing that brought different perspectives to what the world offers. I knew I wanted to live in a world where all differences were embraced, create safe spaces for connection and sharing our authentic stories and backgrounds, and celebrate unity in diversity. My Armenian father, who I adored, came to the United States as an immigrant would always share this powerful quote from Gandhi. "Our ability to reach unity in diversity will be the beauty and test of our civilization." For so long, what that meant for me was to embrace other people's differences and foster inclusion. The defining moment in my life to create a sense of belonging and connection to action was when my three-year-old son was diagnosed with ASD or Autism Syndrome Disorder. Shortly after, I completely changed my career path from sales and marketing to become a Diversity, Equity, and Inclusion practitioner within organizations. My goal was to create impactful, equitable, and inclusive long-term sustainable strategies that foster a sense of belonging for all employees. All people deserve to feel like they can be their most authentic selves, tap into their inner genius, and feel accepted. Having many vulnerable conversations with underrepresented individuals like people of color, women, people with invisible and visible disabilities, and LGBTQI+ individuals, to name a few, I quickly learned that finding belonging and connection, which is core human needs, start with belonging and connecting to oneself. As a life empowerment coach who is also on my self-discovery journey, I've found that creating a safe space to embody your emotions and build a sense of resilience and comfort in facing any strong emotions is where true belonging happens. This connection to yourself and your feelings is super important for true belonging, starting with allowing and facing any emotion or feeling without avoidance and judgment. So, what do I mean when I say own your authentic power through belonging and connection?

Like the well-known author, Gary Zukav says "Authentic power is the energy formed by the intentions of the Soul. It is the light shaped by the intentions of love and compassion guided by wisdom." It begins with becoming deeply curious about who you are and what motivates you. Then, it can start with practicing self-acceptance, self-compassion, and self-love. So, I welcome you to use the questions below to explore where you are in your journey right now. You can use a journal or write in the space provided below.

What is your connection to your purpose, set of values, goals, and beliefs?

What are your core values and beliefs?

What set of values guide you in your life?

What thoughts or emotions do you need to address that get in your way to reclaim your life?

How do you protect yourself from the judgment of others?

Positive Self-Talk:

As I learn and discover my own life's journey, practicing self-acceptance can be quite a challenge. Sometimes, I would find myself at work not sharing my voice because, just like when I was that little girl, I wanted to fit in. In addition, I was confronted with the inner thoughts of conforming to what others believed I needed to be or what society expected of me.

This was something I desperately wanted to change. So I learned to use a daily practice of positive self-talk to bring more self-acceptance and self-compassion. A positive self-talk is a powerful tool that works for many, including me.

It may seem obvious but let me tell you what I mean by "positive self-talk." Positive self-talk is _speaking_ to yourself and _treating_ yourself with kindness and compassion, just like treating someone you care about. This practice is part of positive psychology, and it's about leaning into your strengths rather than focusing solely on your weaknesses. It is not about always being positive, but about a neutral way of interacting with your thoughts and feelings more compassionately. It helped reframe **_how_** I spoke to myself and taught me to speak with love, grace, compassion, and kindness.

Here are some examples of positive self-talk statements that you can try right now:
- I love myself for who I truly am
- I am in complete control of my emotions
- Fear is only a feeling; it cannot hold me back
- I am grateful for everything I have in my life
- I am a magnet for positivity, abundance, and happiness
- I have the power to be happy regardless
- I am enough
- I am loved

Self-Love:
Self-love means setting boundaries.
As a mother, wife, and career woman, I struggled with self-compassion and self-love throughout my life. I was constantly putting others before me and forgetting about my self-care. I was working at an organization feeling like I had to please others and work around the clock between my professional career and juggling priorities for my family until my body officially shut down. I ended up falling to the ground in immense pain and rushed to the emergency room. For the first time, I had kidney stones, and that experience was a big wake-up call to take care of myself first to sustain my passion and purpose for my life and be there for my family.

That experience led me to understand my love for true belonging. Brené Brown, a research professor, and author, talks about two aspects of true belonging: you can share your most authentic self and the other to be who you are. So we can truly accept ourselves first and have more self-compassion and self-love, we can lean into our vulnerability and show our unique and authentic selves. One of my favorite quotes from Brené Brown says, *"True belonging is the spiritual practice of believing in and belonging to yourself so deeply that you can share your most authentic self with the world and find sacredness in both being a part of something and standing alone in the wilderness. True belonging doesn't require you to change who you are; it requires you to be who you are."* – Brené Brown

Sharing one powerful tip from my learned experience of showing my vulnerability is having the power to set boundaries around my values.

Oprah Winfrey once said, *"You have to be able to set boundaries; otherwise, the rest of the world is telling you who you are and what you should be doing. You can still be a nice person and set boundaries. It feels great to connect to people, but having boundaries is so important."*

So, what do I mean by personal boundaries? The Resilience Centre says it best as personal boundaries are guidelines, rules, or limits that a person creates to identify reasonable, safe, and permissible ways for other people to behave towards them and how they will respond when someone passes those limits. They are built out of a mix of beliefs, attitudes, past experiences, and social learning. Personal boundaries help define an individual by outlining likes and dislikes and setting the distance one allows others to approach.

Setting healthy boundaries can improve self-esteem, self-worth, and a personal comfort level that will leave you feeling energized. Here are some steps to set up some healthy boundaries for yourself. Certainly, these can look different for each unique individual, and I welcome you to craft ones that would work best for you. The key is to be brave enough to start the process and implement them. It's not about being perfect.

Some things that have worked for me were to evaluate what I valued and what I want to prioritize in my life. It was taking inventory of what matters. After meditation, I remember getting out a piece of paper and drawing a huge circle. In the center were

ME and my purpose. To serve my purpose in a way that also fuels my wellbeing, I had to ask myself the questions of what are my values? Who are the essential relationships that fuel my soul? How can I live my best life? I started there and quickly realized that parts of my life I was prioritizing didn't align with my values and I quickly shifted and 'dropped the ball, which the amazing author Tiffany Dufu says in her book, "Drop the Ball."

Secondly, meditation and self-reflection became my daily habit. We all have biases, and all our brains are wired for it. Spending time daily to pause and reflect on how I perceive the world and recognize the shifts I need to make into higher consciousness has been one of the most profound ways of creating healthy boundaries for myself.

Lastly, it was recognizing and embracing the thought of being perfectly imperfect. What do I mean by embracing being perfectly imperfect? Let me tell you what happened with my daughter and me. I remember we were on vacation, and she and I were walking on the beach when she found a giant seashell. It was a beautiful seashell, but it had one obvious flaw. It had a crack right through its center. She was so excited to find this big shell, and she goes, "Mom, I'm excited I found this big seashell, but I can't keep it because it's broken." Recognizing this could be a great learning moment, my answer to her was to look at the beauty of this shell and embrace the perfectly imperfect seashell. The crack is where the light comes in!

I shared a quote that my father would always tell me from Rumi, a famous Persian Poet and Scholar who said, "The wound is the place where the light enters you." Then, I shared with her the concept about how the Japanese fill cracks in broken pottery with gold-dusted lacquer in the centuries-old art of Kintsugi. By adding beauty and uniqueness to what is broken, they emphasize the fractures instead of hiding them. And while Kintsugi blocks the light that could shine through the cracks, seeing beauty in the flawed (the Japanese philosophy of wabi-sabi) is what we can celebrate.

After weaving a perfect rug, I also once read that The Navajo interrupt one stitch to "let the world in."

A crack is where the light comes in.
A wound is a place where the light enters.
A fracture allows beauty from brokenness.
A stitch of imperfection lets the world in.

This shell became one of our family's most teachable moments that we all have parts of us that are "cracked" or what we consider broken. Still, when we can empower ourselves to see the beauty and purpose each of us holds, we can embrace all the perfectly imperfect beings we are.

My daughter did take the seashell home and now has it on her desk in her room. It is a constant reminder to look at our life experiences through a lens of learning and letting the world in through our imperfections. It's a feeling of empowerment to make decisions based on our values and is the start of true belonging. When I can belong to myself, I can share my best self with others and continue living my purpose of empowering people to feel seen, heard, embraced, valued, celebrated, and loved so humanity can transcend and thrive.

Embrace the beautiful human you are and fully live presently in your journey of connecting and belonging to yourself so you can, in turn, share your bright light and create a world filled with love. Whether it's motivational speaking, empowerment coaching, or consulting, I welcome you to join Ignite Inclusion at www.igniteinclusion.com and follow me on this journey to own your authentic power through belonging and connection!

ABOUT THE AUTHOR

Christine Ramsay (She/Her/Hers) is a first-generation Armenian American whose life purpose is to create a world where all people feel seen, heard, valued, celebrated, and loved so they continue to thrive and ignite their happiness.

She is Chief Empowerment Officer and Founder of Ignite Inclusion, LLC whose mission is to help individuals and organizations unlock their inner genius and discover their potential by taking control of their happiness and wellbeing. Our vision is to create an inclusive culture of happiness where all humans feel seen, heard, valued, celebrated, and loved for seeing the world differently. Our mission is to help people, organizational leaders and teams, and communities continue to thrive and take control of their own happiness by building habits that create life-work flow.

She is a Certified Happiness and Leadership Coach, TEDx and motivational speaker, Certified coach in Brain Based Skills Neuroscience of Inclusion, Certified coach for Social and Emotional Intelligence (EI), and a Certified Diversity Professional (CDP).

She is a parent advocate for Gender inclusion, Autism & Neurodiversity, Well-being and Happiness. She has spoken at major big conferences such as the Gross Happiness Summit for the University of Peace hosted by the United Nations, SHRM and ATD national conferences, many podcasts, and been interviewed by leading best-selling author and entrepreneur voices such as Tiffany Dufu and Claudia Chan.

She currently lives outside of Philadelphia with her spouse and two children. Christine enjoys spending time with family and traveling all over the world.

www.igniteinclusion.com
SOCIAL HANDLE: @Igniteinclusion

Your Life Is Worth It!

Made in the USA
Columbia, SC
28 February 2022